Please renew/return this item by the last date shown.

So that your telephon
please call the numbe

From Area ts:
01923 or (

Renewals: 01923 471
Enquiries: 01923 471333   01438 737333
Minicom: 01923 471599   01438 737599

L32b

CAMBRIDGE MONOGRAPHS IN
EXPERIMENTAL BIOLOGY
No. 12

EDITORS:
T. A. BENNET-CLARK
GEORGE SALT (*General Editor*)
C. H. WADDINGTON, V. B. WIGGLESWORTH

BIRD-SONG

THE SERIES

BIRD-SONG

*The Biology of Vocal Communication
and Expression in Birds*

BY

W. H. THORPE

Sc.D., F.R.S.

*Reader in Animal Behaviour in the
University of Cambridge and
Fellow of Jesus College*

CAMBRIDGE
AT THE UNIVERSITY PRESS
1961

PUBLISHED BY
THE SYNDICS OF THE CAMBRIDGE UNIVERSITY PRESS

Bentley House, 200 Euston Road, London, N.W. 1
American Branch: 32 East 57th Street, New York 22, N.Y.
West African Office: P.O. Box 33, Ibadan, Nigeria

©

CAMBRIDGE UNIVERSITY PRESS
1961

Printed in Great Britain at the University Press, Cambridge
(Brooke Crutchley, University Printer)

CONTENTS

v

PREFACE

DURING the last twenty years the study of animal vocalisations has been revolutionised by the development of high quality recording, especially on tape, and the spectrographic analysis of sounds. It is the object of this book to survey recent developments in the study of bird songs and call notes, especially those which have resulted from modern experimental techniques and the exploitation of these new methods. The book does not set out to be a general treatise on bird vocal communication, but only on some of these recently developed aspects of its study. It is in some degree complementary to a book entitled *A Study of Bird Song*, by Rev. E. A. Armstrong (Oxford University Press) which will cover a wide area of non-experimental field work and will be invaluable to those who require a general summary of recent work on this subject by naturalists.

I have received a great deal of help in many aspects of my work, help without which the production of the book would not have been possible. The British Broadcasting Corporation in 1953 deposited with the Department of Zoology in Cambridge a complete set of their bird song recordings, including all the pioneer recordings by Dr Ludwig Koch, and they have kept the series up to date by frequent additions as new recordings were processed. Similarly the Laboratory of Ornithology of Cornell University, Ithaca, New York, has been extremely helpful in supplying material. Much of the earlier stages of the work was accomplished in collaboration with Dr Peter Marler who was my research assistant during the period 1952–7 under a grant from the Nature Conservancy. I am most grateful to the Nature Conservancy for making Dr Marler's work possible. To Dr R. J. Andrew, Dr Lars von Haartmann and Dr Fae Hall I am much indebted for providing material for special illustrations and figures. Miss Barbara Lade has been responsible for preparing a great many of the illustrations which are, of course, a quite indispensable feature of the book. I am most grateful to her for this, and for her help in many other ways. I have received valuable comment on different parts of the manuscript from Rev. E. A. Armstrong and Dr J. Beament. Dr G. Salt,

F.R.S., in his capacity as one of the editors of the series, made a number of valuable suggestions and took a helpful interest in various stages of the book's production. I am also greatly indebted to Miss E. M. Barraud for her work in typing the manuscript and in checking and preparing the list of references and compiling the indexes.

In a book dealing mainly with birds whose English names are so well standardised and so widely known it would seem cumbersome and pedantic to add the scientific names generally throughout the pages. Consequently the English names have been used in the text but where they have a clear *specific* connotation they have, as in the previous ornithological volume in this series, been capitalised. Thus the eye can pick out at a glance what species is being discussed even if the italicised scientific names are omitted; these can of course be ascertained from the index of birds at the end.

W.H.T.

JESUS COLLEGE
CAMBRIDGE

April 1961

NOTE ON THE ILLUSTRATIONS

THE illustrations in this book are mainly exact or diagrammatic reproductions of sound spectrograms. For examples of spectrograms of normal songs of familiar species, see figs. 21, 22, 26 and 27. The sound spectrograph was originally invented by the staff of the Bell Telephone Laboratories and has in recent years been manufactured commercially by Kay Electric Company of New Jersey, under the commercial name of 'Sonograph'. Description of this and other techniques for recording and analysing bird vocalisations will be found in Potter, Kopp and Green (1947), Joos (1948) and Thorpe (1958a).

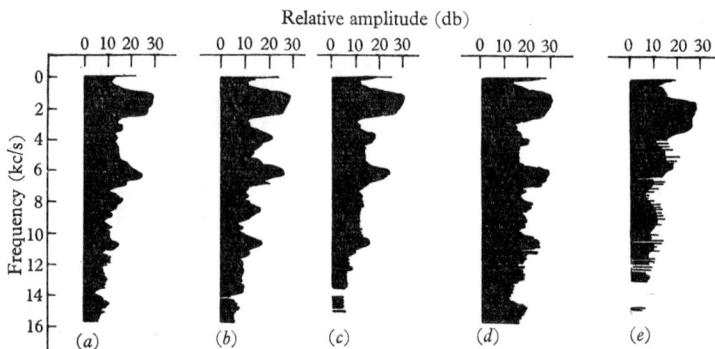

Fig. 1. Nightingale. Amplitude section through five notes of Nightingale song shown in fig. 28.

Sound spectrograms give a graphic representation of frequency ('pitch'), amplitude ('loudness') and duration which can with practice be recognised and interpreted as a 'picture' of the sound. Unless otherwise stated, the ordinate represents frequency in kilocycles per second, and the abscissa time in seconds. The accuracy limits are 45 cycles and 0·0015 s. The apparatus thus supplies a form of notation as well as a method of precise measurement. Used in this way, amplitude is represented by depth of shading and is approximate only. If it is desired to study relative amplitude more precisely, the apparatus can be used to give what is known as an 'amplitude section' (fig. 1). In an amplitude section the time component is eliminated and the machine gives a graph at any required instant (in effect covering a period of about $\frac{1}{24}$ s) of the relative amplitude in decibels of a given note of the song expressed against frequency in kilocycles per second. The allocation, as between different frequencies, of the total energy expended in producing a given note is thus shown, and if the note has any

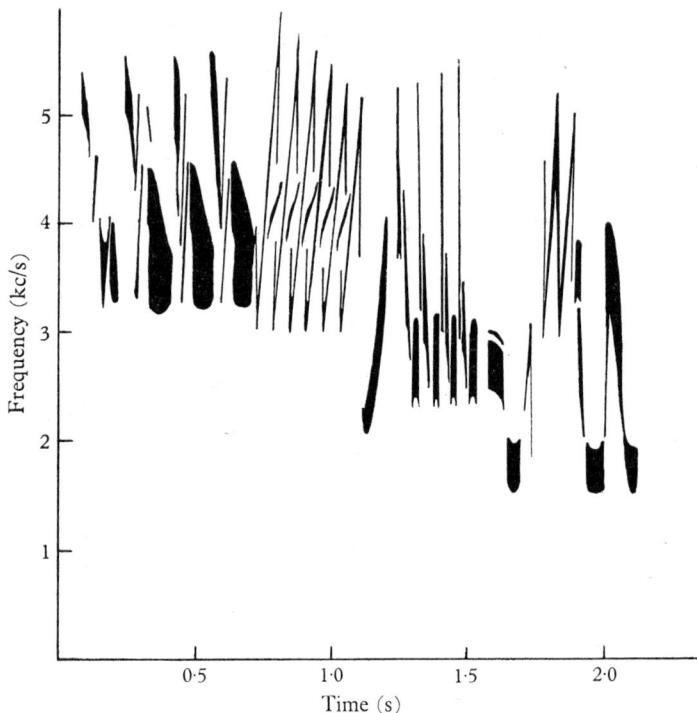

Fig. 2. Chaffinch. Simplified form of sound spectrogram adequate for many purposes. Compare with fig. 18.

sort of 'musical' structure this will be indicated by a large hump at some lower frequency (this being the fundamental) and a series of smaller humps at higher frequency, which may represent harmonics. Marler and Isaac (1960) have described a valuable new device for producing a series of amplitude sections separated by a time interval of as little as 2·5 ms.

Since the degree to which the sound is concentrated in this way is largely responsible for the resulting tonal quality, it is

x

thus possible with practice to tell from the sound spectrogram approximately how the note will sound to the human ear. If the energy is not concentrated systematically at any particular related points, but is spread more or less at random over the frequency length, then the sound is likely to be harsh and discordant. A pure sound, on the other hand, will show either as a simple note of small frequency range or, if the frequency range is large, the sound spectrogram will indicate a strong fundamental and a series of six or more quite discrete harmonics at related intervals above it—the harmonics 3, 5 and 7 (the fundamental being 1) being stronger, and the even-numbered ones somewhat weaker. Such a frequency distribution will tend to give a richness and quality to the tone.

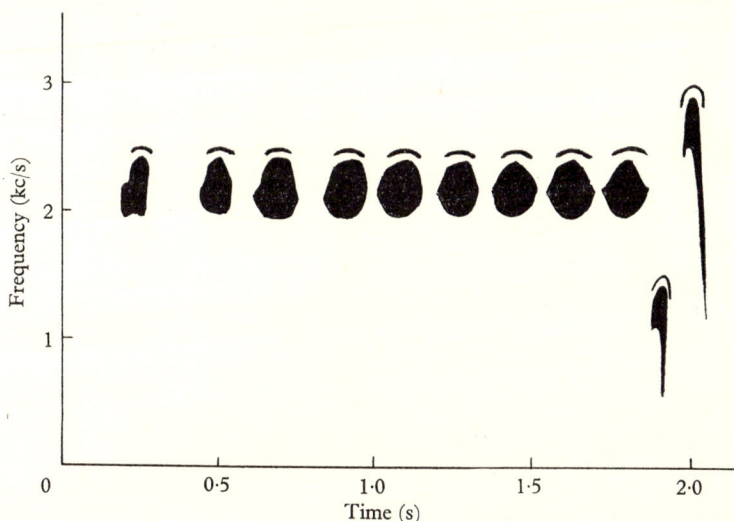

Fig. 3. Nightingale. Simplified form of sound spectrogram. Compare with fig. 28.

There is now a new form of the sound spectrograph, developed and elaborated by Gunnar Fant (1958) in Stockholm, which carries out a simultaneous frequency and amplitude analysis without interruption. This apparatus is, however, so elaborate and costly that it will be a long time before it comes into general use for zoological work, if indeed it ever does so.

Besides the sound spectrograph, W. R. Fish (1953) has described a direct-inking magnetic oscillograph method for studying bird-song. As described, this instrument does not measure amplitude (although this measurement can be made by relatively simple additions) and there are many factors contributing to tonal quality which also cannot be measured. The chief advantage of the apparatus is that it can be constructed entirely from spare parts obtainable from standard radio dealers, and can be put together by a person moderately competent in the electronics of radio receivers.

An ingenious earlier method for investigation of bird-songs will be found in papers by Metfessel (1928, 1929 and 1934) and Ingraham (1938). Apart from such methods, all the early attempts to provide a notation for bird-song consisted essentially in what one might call aural or freehand attempts to make a Fourier analysis, and they thus resemble crude attempts at producing a sound spectrogram. Useful examples of such *ad hoc* systems of notation are provided by the work of Falconer (1941) and Saunders (1935).

For many purposes of the student of bird behaviour, and for the general ornithologist, sound spectrograms contain a great deal more information than is relevant to the particular point at issue; so it is sometimes advantageous to reproduce them in a somewhat diagrammatic and stereotyped form which draws attention to the main items of information without confusing the picture with a great deal of irrelevant detail. Figs. 2, 3 and 26 provide examples of a simplified or stylised mode of representation of sound spectrograms which is adequate for most purposes of the field ornithologist and is easier and less expensive to reproduce (Thorpe and Lade, 1961).

CHAPTER I

Bird-song as Music and as Language, and Methods for its Study

T H E title of this book begs a question: this is because of the world-wide use of the term 'song' to denote the more complex utterances of the majority of the smaller birds of the world. The word song invariably implies a form of music, and the reader may justifiably object that song is a human art form and nothing else. But though the title of *Bird Vocalisations*—which is almost the only practical alternative—would have been both more accurate and more objective in its implications, there is no other argument in its favour, so *Bird-Song* the book must be called.

This almost universal conviction that the more complex utterances of birds do constitute a form of art is worth a moment's consideration. Not long ago the President of the Royal Academy of Art roundly abused the Director of the British Museum of Natural History for speaking of the results of chimpanzee experiments with paint as 'paintings', implying (as he undoubtedly did) that they show the first glimmerings of artistic sensibility. I think it is inconceivable that the President of the Royal Academy of Music should abuse me or any other author for writing a book upon the subject of bird-song. But is there anything behind this universal popular conviction that birds sing, in the sense of making music? If we ask the musician or the musicologist to define music, we are likely to get a confusing answer. According to Redfield (1935), there are eight factors involved in music: melody, harmony, rhythm, form, tempo, dynamics, tone colour and nuance. A moment's thought will serve to show that all except harmony, and possibly nuance (which is so vague an idea as to be difficult to assess in this connection) are present in innumerable examples of bird-song; and even the absence of harmony does not seem to be very fundamental since it has been truly said that harmony is, after all, merely simultaneous instead of successive melody. Rhythm there certainly is: rhythm has to do with the relative stress of musical tone, stress being given to a tone either by accenting it or by increasing its duration. To many of us brought up in the western musical tradition, much bird-song may appear to be a-rhythmic, but this is incorrect and is due to confusion between measure and rhythm. Music is regarded as measured when there is throughout the composition a steady recurrence of rhythmic stress or accent, so that the music divides itself into measures or bars. Though very little bird music is measured, it is none-the-less rhythmic. That bird-song has form is self-evident: if it had not, we could not remember it. That it has tempo is also obvious, for tempo is the rhythm's rate of progress.

Another way of defining music is to regard it as simply a patterning of sound. If we adopt this wider definition, then certainly, as Herzog says (1941), we can hardly deny that animals and birds make music. Music is of course a particular type of sound patterning, implying (according to Herzog) the use of fixed points in pitch, tones and transposition. These fixed points and the use of them can be found in bird-song essentially because the bird's ear works—so we have every reason to believe—in very much the same way as the human ear. Thus if a bird is to produce a sound-pattern recognisable and distinctive to other members of its species, it will also have some of the characteristics which we regard as musical. But music is also an art and, to quote Redfield again, 'the art of music consists in the utilisation of these various characters...in such a manner that the result produced is recognised by us as beautiful. If rhythm alone, or melody or harmony alone, produce what is beautiful, then it is music.'

Although the simplest definition of music does imply changes varying round certain fixed points in pitch—that is to say, tones—and transpositions of such variations, it need not necessarily include even this. For instance, transposition is unknown in many simple musical styles and animals do not utter their calls always in the same pitch. In fact it is possible to arrange all types of sound-pattern into one series, starting with music on instruments of fixed pitch and including vocal expressions of animals and birds as well as the melodic inflections of human speech. Again quoting Herzog, 'from the purely formal point of view, there thus seems to be no reliable criterion that would

2

establish a fundamental difference between animal and human expression in sound'.

Almost every reader of this book will have heard enough bird-song to be able to think for himself of examples illustrating these various elements of true music. As regards beauty of individual notes, the flute-like sounds which are by no means uncommon in bird-songs provide excellent instances. Thus the notes of the Pileated Tinamou of Central America perhaps strike our ears as beautiful as any natural sounds in the world. Hartshorne (1958) similarly quotes the Pied Butcher-bird of Australia as comparable in quality to a fine flute. Besides beauty

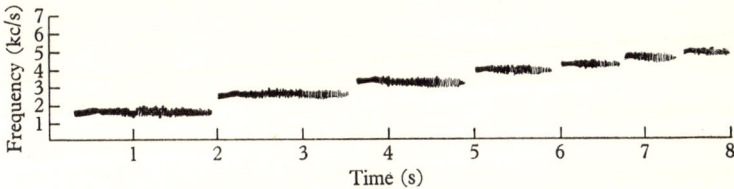

Fig. 4. Song of Pileated Tinamou. Note the grouping of notes at a steadily rising pitch and steadily decreasing length. Note purity of the tone giving a flute-like impression to the ear, each note commencing with a simple pure sound of slightly rising pitch which then falls again and starts to break up into pulses giving a rich tremolando effect which fades away gradually towards the end of the note. The pattern of the individual notes is based on Cornell recordings from Costa Rica; information as to pitch is approximate only.

of tone colour, the song of the Tinamou above mentioned illustrates in elementary fashion the beauty of rhythm, tempo and dynamics (fig. 4). When we come to examine them, hardly any bird-songs are random handfuls of notes, and it is hard to find a song of more than a few seconds' duration that does not display several of the above-mentioned characteristics of music. But although we can find some beauty in almost all bird-songs, the persistent reiteration of the territorial songs of some species has sometimes a maddening monotony to human ears. As Hartshorne (1956) points out, however, few bird-songs are so stereotyped as to be unendurably monotonous on repetition, and it is surprising how extensively his 'anti-monotony principle' appears to apply in bird-song. When we listen to them carefully, the slight variations in many songs are sufficient to reduce, if not altogether eliminate, the sense of monotony.

Another characteristic which we note so often in bird-song is the appearance, within a single song or phrase, of repetitional likeness between successive portions. This is in accordance with the general aesthetic principle of unity in variety, and perhaps it is this single factor more than any other upon which the appeal of bird-song to the human ear rests; but—as we shall see in chapter 4—there are biological reasons adequate to explain many of the phenomena. This variety in unity, illustrated in an elementary form by songs such as that of the Black-capped Chickadee, perhaps reaches its finest expression in the songs of some of our thrushes and in the Rocky Mountain Solitaire. This bird often sings continuously for 20 s a song which must be one of the most complicated in the world, having a remarkable structural beauty. When we listen intently to other songs such as those of the European Wren, the American Winter Wren, the Song Thrush, the Blackbird or the Skylark, we find that there is an extraordinary degree of individual variation which nevertheless is not such as to leave any doubt in the listener's mind as to the identity of the species. To Hartshorne the one great deficiency, from the musical point of view, of bird-song is the extremely brief temporal span of the motifs or musical units. It seems as if a bird cannot follow a definite musical pattern occupying more than 10 s—seldom, in fact, more than 6 s—and it is estimated that the average for all singing birds is probably a unit of less than 3 s. This temporal limitation of the motifs of bird-song, while striking to our ears, does not of course necessarily imply that the songs are short from the bird's point of view. As we shall see later, there is very good evidence that birds have a shorter 'time perception smear'—that is, they are able to perceive as distinct notes which follow one another in such quick succession that to our ears they merge as a single unit; indeed the Winter Wren is able to include in its song a succession of about three hundred notes all within a time of about 8 s. But I think we can agree with the provisional hypothesis of Hartshorne that birds do about as much 'musically' as can possibly be done with a very few short units of design, and on the whole without polyphony. It would be hard to find a better example of a well-balanced melodic line than the phrase (fig. 5) from the song of the Wood Pewee.

But of course it is entirely unjustifiable to conclude that because many bird-songs sound beautiful to our ears, they necessarily seem beautiful to the bird. Conversely, of course,

4

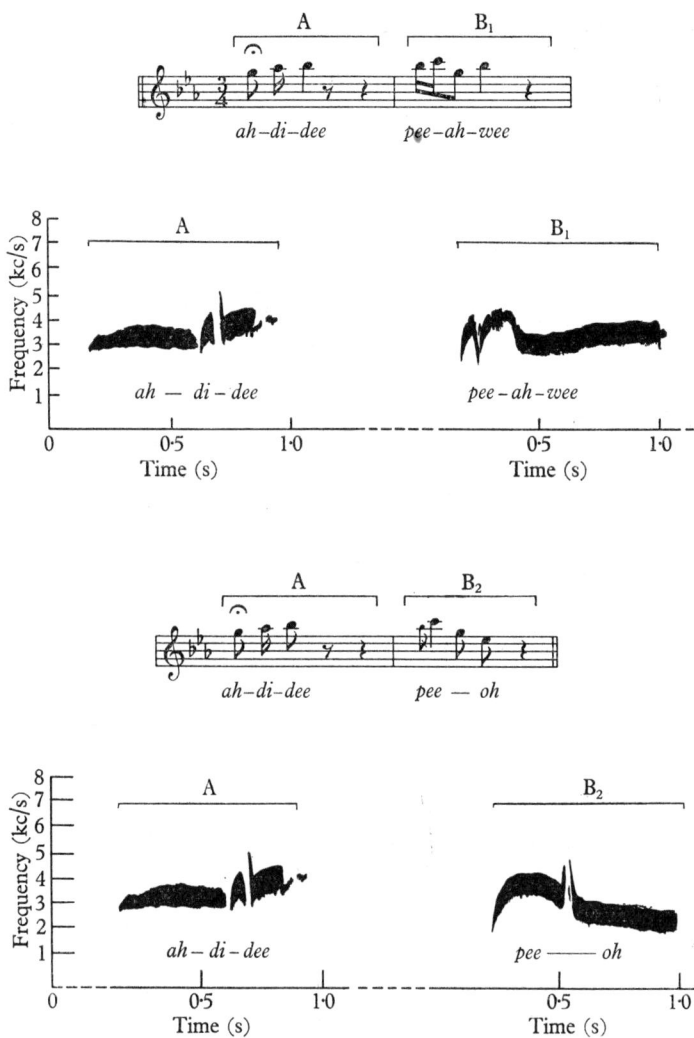

Fig. 5. Wood Pewee. An example of a well-balanced melodic line. This is one of the rather few bird-songs which can be adequately rendered in musical notation. (Craig, 1943, and Cornell recording.)

many animal-sounds which seem hideous to our ears may, for all we know, appear entrancingly beautiful to the performers themselves. The judgement of musical beauty is a personal judgement depending upon an emotional relationship between the music and the hearer, derived from his past experience and social environment, which largely determines his decision as to what is beautiful. Although I think we shall be able to show with a good deal of plausibility that there are some species which give evidence of individual development and organisation of songs which suggests artistic creativeness, these species are very exceptional as far as we at present know. Moreover, the final criterion for artistic activity, namely the desire or intention to express or create something of beauty or significance, must remain in doubt.

The following pages will show that there are many excellent biological and physiological explanations of a great deal of bird-song and sound production. It would, however, be dishonest to suggest that the biological theories at present available offer a complete explanation for all bird vocalisations. There are many instances of songs which seem to transcend biological requirements and suggest that the bird is actively seeking new auditory and vocal experience—'playing with sounds', so to speak—and that this may represent the beginnings of a true artistic activity. Thus the twilight song of the Wood Pewee appears to have no territorial function and is said to be independent of the breeding-cycle, and the day-time song also continues long after the end of the breeding-season. Bicknell (1884–5) concludes that the song of late summer and autumn is, in many American song birds, superior to that of the breeding-season. Noble (1931) records that the duration of the Skylark's song is greatest in September and October, and Saunders (1929) has observed in many species of American song birds the lengthening, elaboration and sometimes complete change in the song after the end of the nesting period. These changes often seem, to our ears, to take the form of an aesthetic improvement and Saunders suggests that the song is improved at this time because it no longer needs to remain in the simple form of the territorial song. Haecker (1900 and 1916) comes to a similar conclusion with regard to the autumn and winter singing of Central European song birds, and Böker (1923) supports Haecker's thesis with histological evidence, examination of the testes of autumn- and winter-singing birds showing no suggestion of an unusually high level of sex hormone production. On the other hand, Davis (1958) shows a very close and detailed correlation between secretory activity of the testis and the song period of the Rufous-sided Towhee.

6

We might of course expect, as Nicholson (1927) has pointed out, that birds that hold winter territories might sing in the winter more than do other species. It is difficult to get reliable evidence on this point because so often our criterion for assuming winter territorialism is the occurrence of song, but even if there is a close correlation, this does not seem to offer a satisfactory explanation of the improvement in song during autumn and winter referred to above.

From the evolutionary point of view we cannot of course suppose that a phenomenon so widespread and so striking as bird-song could have arisen merely as an outlet for emotional expression, having no relation with other individuals of the species—that is to say, an expression which, if it had any function at all, could only be regarded as self-relieving or self-stimulating. On the contrary, there are overwhelming reasons for believing that song could only have been evolved for, or in the process of, producing social releasers the object of which is to govern and co-ordinate the behaviour of associated individuals of the same species. All our experience suggests that bird vocalisations are primarily communicatory in function.

In attempting to employ the now popular language of communication theory or information theory in connection with animal behaviour, we must guard against begging the question at the outset by assuming that we are necessarily dealing with the communication of ideas. Communication has been defined (Stevens, 1950) as the discriminatory response of an organism to a stimulus. This is obviously unsatisfactory for, as Cherry (1957) points out, communication is not the response itself but is essentially the relationship set up by the transmission of stimuli and the evocation of responses. We use the response as evidence that there has been communication. Secondly, in this connection it is preferable to employ the more restricted term social releaser rather than stimulus. A stimulus can be any stimulation mediated by the sense organs to which the organism responds. A social releaser is a specific stimulus, or much more often a pattern of stimulation, provided by one member of a species and apparently adapted to the function of influencing the behaviour of other members of the same or of other species. Thus these social releasers are what we should in human terms speak of as 'signals.' If, then, communication is a relationship, the theory of communication is concerned with the measurement of the information content of signals, for on this depends their effectiveness in the establishment of communication links. But the information content of signals is not to be regarded as a commodity; it is more a property or a potential of the signal, and as a concept it is closely related to the idea of selection or discrimination (Cherry). Thus the mathematical theory of information was originally developed in telegraphy and telephony for the purpose of measuring the information content of telecommunication signals. The essential process in signalling is to recognise whether two signals are the same or different—that is to say: Are the signals the same? 'Yes'; or not the same, 'No'. 'Any message which is expressed in language may be written in binary code, as a series of yes-es and no-s, or 1 and 0, and is said to be logically communicable.' Such an individual single choice of Yes against No, or 1 against 0, is called a binary digit, or 'bit' for short. And these bits are the fundamental units of information of any code or system of communication. But the sense organs of men and animals are continually being bombarded by all kinds of stimuli of which the meaningful ones from the fellow member of the species may be infrequent or hard to perceive. If a communication channel is to be effective in practice, whether it be a telephone line, a radio wave, a human sentence or a bird-song, it must have some resistance to interruption, some ability to be received in spite of the competition from innumerable meaningless sensory events accompanying it. It can do this by being frequently repeated and/or displaying different qualities or characteristics simultaneously, as in sound signals such as speech which is varying simultaneously in frequency, amplitude and time characteristic—in other words, undergoing frequency modulation, amplitude modulation and temporal modulation. Thus that communication system will be most efficient which contains enough repetition or redundancy of information to ensure that its message gets through; and those species will be most successful in communication which have sense organs and central nervous system capable of accepting a generous supply of signal information and storing that which is relevant. Thus in the evolution of communication systems the conflicting requirements of, on the one hand, the ability to transmit a large amount of information about many different circumstances and, on the other hand, the necessity of making sure that important information always gets through, must always have been present and in competition. The communication systems of animals can therefore be regarded as exemplifying a compromise between conflicting requirements, and as we study bird-song and call-notes we shall see ample evidence that this is so.

The question then is: How far can bird vocalisations be regarded as a form of language?

The methods of communication employed by animals are very various. Visual signals and displays or gestures (from the dances of bees to the displays of birds), odour trails and the marking of territory by excreta and the secretions of special glands are all common and widespread in the mammals and the social insects. Much sex behaviour is also initiated and controlled by sensitivity to special secretions, as with the dog seeking the bitch on heat. Less usual, but nevertheless well known, is the use of movable objects, animate or inanimate, as 'symbols' or 'tokens'—as in courtship feeding, prey exchange and nest relief ceremonies.

Each of these methods no doubt has its advantages, but they all have great limitations compared with the use of mechanical vibrations of a medium—especially the air—as signals. Spiders of course can obtain certain information as the result of per-ceiving the vibrations of the web, and rabbits signal by thumping the ground. But the great advantage of the use of airborne or waterborne vibrations, namely 'sounds', as signals is that sound carries far and fast and readily by-passes obstacles, there is a great spectrum of frequency and intensity available for use, it is extremely economical to produce, and—since sounds vanish as quickly as they are produced—the items of information do not accumulate so as to prevent the sending of further messages. So it is obvious why a language, if it is to achieve its full potentialities, must be a language of sounds. The language of sounds has been brought to a high degree of development by the insects, the Amphibia, the birds and the mammals; perhaps also by the fish—which would be expected, because a sound wave travels farther, for a given loss of amplitude, in water than in air, and also approximately four times as fast—although we have as yet almost everything to learn about the significance of sound production by fishes. Other animal groups which have gone in for sound language have not as yet raised it beyond a rather primitive level.

But much if not all of the phenomenon called 'language' in animals is something very different from human speech. A great deal of the language of animals depends upon an innate ability to produce the required sounds or make the appropriate actions, and an inherent ability to respond, by means of inborn mechanisms. Thus though the hearer shows by its behaviour that 'information has been received' (as when a Chaffinch takes cover from a hawk on hearing the *seeee* alarm call), the response we observe may be largely or entirely innately controlled and does not imply that the 'recipient makes a conscious assessment of the information contained in the call' (Marler, 1956), although this may of course occur as well. However, no one with any knowledge of bird behaviour will doubt that in bird language we have something much more than a system of instinctive vocal signals—although this is just what call-notes mainly seem to be. Some species of bird can undoubtedly augment the innate repertoire of sounds which they utter and to which they respond, by a simple conditioning or trial-and-error learning (Thorpe, 1956); for example, the *kiau* call of the Herring Gull (Goethe, 1954) and the flight call of the Linnet (Poulsen 1954).[1] This again need not involve any conscious assessment on the part of the bird. But one has only to keep a parrot to know that vocal utterances can be acquired not only by conditioning, but also by an apparently much more complex process of imitative learning which sometimes involves considerable practice, and there is no doubt at all that a great many bird utterances are learned or conditioned in one way or another by past experience.

It used at one time to be argued that there exists a fundamental difference between the language of animals and that of man in that, so it was stated, animal language is emotive only, while the language of humans is both emotive and propositional—that is, able to convey precise information as distinct from inducing a particular mood in the hearer. The recognition of the bees' dance as a language has already disposed of that particular distinction since the 'waggle dance' of the hive bee can convey precise information (again not necessarily consciously assessed) as to distance and direction of a food source.

But even if some animals do consciously understand their

[1] Other less well established instances of supposedly innate call notes being influenced by learning are mentioned by Lanyon and Tavolga (1960, p. 329).

languages (as there seems to be little doubt they do), there still remain of course profound differences between the even most elaborate animal language and human speech which is acquired by learning processes of great complexity. Our use of language involves an ability to represent or symbolise completely abstract or general ideas by words which *in themselves* have nothing of the essential characteristics of the concepts which they denote—the word 'three', for instance, has nothing triple about it, nor is 'four' quadruple. As far as we yet know for certain, no animal language, however much information may be conveyed, involves the learnt realisation of completely general abstractions of this kind—although recent studies have been reported which make it seem more probable than heretofore. This cannot be dealt with here. The evidence for 'thinking without words' (ideation) among birds which has emerged from the monumental studies of Otto Koehler and his pupils at Freiburg has been summarised by Thorpe (1956, pp. 119, 340–9). Koehler himself (1956) concludes that, however great the gulf which divides animal from human language, there is no single characteristic which can be used as an absolutely infallible criterion for distinguishing bird from human language. Rather, human speech is unique only in the way in which it combines attributes which in themselves are not peculiar to man but are found also in more than one group of animals.

However, this book is concerned not only with the function of song as language, but even more with the problems involved in the behavioural and neural mechanisms whereby the songs are acquired and elaborated. When we consider bird-song as a pattern of neuro-muscular activity, we at once see its extraordinary physiological interest. Here we have a set of discrete but co-ordinated movements carried out by a set of up to six pairs of muscles, producing a song of a few seconds' duration yet consisting of perhaps several hundred separate actions. In some species these actions are so precisely controlled as to be characteristic of the species as such. In other, imitative, birds such as the Indian Hill Mynah, an individual may be capable of producing on the one hand a series of cries, shrill, raucous or guttural as the case may be, or combinations of all three, and on the other hand, the finest nuances of human speech, including individual niceties of vowel production.

It is only comparatively recently that, because of the

development of modern techniques of sound recording and analysis these extraordinary examples of animal behaviour have become amenable to scientific investigation.

The mere recording of a bird's song itself opens up great possibilities for further study. Not only is there the obvious and immense advantage that the records can be played over repeatedly till all aspects of the sound can be memorised; still more valuable is the ability to slow down playback, thus magnifying the time-scale and decreasing the pitch-scale and so bringing the sound-pattern more into the range with which the human ear is adapted to deal.

Once the sound is recorded, it can then, of course, be analysed by oscillographic methods. By this means the exact wave-form of the sound can be obtained, and theoretically every essential feature of the sound extracted for analysis. In practice, however, complete analysis of a sound by oscillographic methods is feasible only with sounds which are maintained at fairly constant frequency and intensity over an appreciable time. Sound-patterns consisting of pulses of very short duration, great frequency range and rapid amplitude and frequency modulation such as are characteristic of bird-song, can only be analysed oscillographically at an utterly prohibitive cost of time and effort. The sound spectrograph has supplied the hoped-for answer to the problem. This is a machine which produces essentially a Fourier analysis of frequency against time. Human hearing, of course, depends upon an analysis of this type, and all the evidence goes to show that the bird hears in approximately the same manner. This fact is of the greatest importance for the student of bird-song, for it is thus relatively easy for us to understand and investigate the significance of bird sounds which normally come within our auditory range. The hearing organs of arthropods, by contrast, are very different. They are extremely sensitive to amplitude modulation, to which certainly the human ear and perhaps also the bird ear is largely insensitive, and extremely insensitive to frequency modulation which is the key to the hearing of mammals and birds.

Almost all the books and papers which give any descriptive account of bird-song will be found to include little mnemonic rhymes or jingles or isolated human words or phrases which are intended to help the reader to remember and compare the specific and individual characteristics of the vocal utterances of birds. These are most helpful if the observer invents them for himself, since they are of necessity highly subjective. They serve first to remind one of the main rhythm of the song, but the vowels do also give one a clue to the relative pitch of different parts of the song, for the vowels in human speech are the elements upon which the pitch primarily depends. But how uncertain and subjective this clue is can be shown by the fact that according to the Germans the cockerel says not *cock-a-doodle-do*, nor even the Shakespearian *cock-a-diddle-dow*, but *kikeriki*, while the Japanese represent it as *Kokke-kokkō* (Cherry, 1957). Thus there is even radical disagreement as to the number of syllables. But I think even Englishmen will agree that the German *zilp-zalp* is a better version of the song of the bird we call Chiffchaff. Perhaps the best standard mnemonic for the Chaffinch is that given by Garstang (1922):

Phrase 1 *a*   Phrase 1 *b*
chip-chip-chip-chip   *tell-tell-tell-tell*

Phrase 2   Phrase 3 *a–b*
cherry-erry-erry-erry   *tissy-che-wee-ooo*

(This should be compared with fig. 18.)

CHAPTER 2

Call-notes

In the previous chapter we discussed bird-song as music, considering it from the point of view of aesthetic judgement. The rest of the book will be devoted to the biological significance of bird vocalisations.

The term 'song' is a convenient one within which to include the varied vocal utterances of a large assemblage of birds, particularly of course the great division of the passerines known as the oscines or song birds. The oscines were originally separated from the rest of the Passeriformes primarily on the basis of the number and complexity of attachment of the syringeal muscles. Within the Passeriformes another group, the sub-oscines, was distinguished from the oscines by having, among other morphological characters, only two or at most three pairs of such muscles. This group, the sub-oscines, includes only two families, both peculiar to Australia, the lyre birds, Menuridae, and the scrub birds, Atrichornithidae. *Atrichornis clamosa* has a 'ringing whistle', oft-repeated and ending in a loud cracking noise; otherwise it does not seem to produce any very notable vocalisation. The Menuridae, on the contrary, have extraordinary vocal powers. The Lyre Bird is said to be able to mimic the calls of owls, laughing jackass, the voices of people, industrial noises and in fact almost any sound which comes to its ears. Lyre birds, moreover, are able to produce a volume of sound which at close quarters can be almost deafening and is said to carry through the forest for a distance of about half a mile. With these examples in front of us, we immediately feel rather diffident about suggesting that vocal ability is correlated with the presence of an elaborate vocal apparatus, for I think the anatomist would have concluded that the syrinx of the sub-oscines could hardly be very effective as a song-producing mechanism. Although, then, this differentiation into oscines and others is in some respects a convenient way of making a broad division in the vast assemblage of birds known as Passeriformes, it does not really help us very much in defining the term 'song' either acoustically or functionally. And it is not in fact possible to draw a hard and fast line between the sounds which constitute call-notes and those which are comprised in the term 'song'. Many examples of 'song' can be found which appear to be little more than a succession of call-notes, for example, among the Limicolae. However, in general it can be said that call-notes are mostly mono- or disyllabic and practically never consist of more than four or five notes. When call-notes are uttered in longer series, then it is without any clear organisation of the sequence into bursts of definite length, the series continuing without interruption as long as the external situation or circumstances and the state of the bird dictate.

What is usually understood by the term song is a series of notes, generally of more than one type, uttered in succession and so related as to form a recognisable sequence or pattern in time. Thus the song as a whole displays the features of accent, increased duration, increased rhythmical complexity, etc. which we were discussing in the first chapter, and which are not discernible to anything like the same extent in call-notes.

When we take into account the function and acoustic characteristics of bird utterances, the definition of song becomes slightly easier, but we still encounter many difficulties. Considering the songs of birds as language does not help us very much further, and still leaves us with the difficulty of distinguishing between call-notes and song. But things are slightly easier if we consider the biological functions of these various utterances. Song is primarily under the control of the sex hormones and is in general concerned with the reproductive cycle, it is of great functional importance in the establishment and defence of territory, often serving as a substitute for physical combat. This function of song as substitute fighting does in fact bear a strikingly close resemblance to song by certain human societies. Lack (1943) has a delightful quotation from Wells's *Outline of History*. This concerns the Bohemian Crusade of 1431 when the Crusaders were encamped in the plain between Domazlice and Horsuv Tyn. 'The Crusaders received the news that the Hussites, under the leadership of Prokop the Great, were approaching. Though the Bohemians were still four miles off, the rattle of their war wagons and the song "All ye warriors of God" which their whole host was chanting could already be heard. The enthusiasm of the Crusaders evaporated with astounding rapidity....The German camp was in utter confusion. Horsemen were streaming off in every direction and the clatter of empty wagons being driven off almost drowned the sound of that terrible singing....So ended the Bohemian Crusade.'

Besides being a substitute for physical combat, song is also— as we shall see in chapter 3—intimately concerned with the maintenance of the pair bond and the mutual adjustment of the sexual cycle of the two members of the pair during its earlier phases. It is thus a form of sexual display. Call-notes, on the other hand, are concerned with the co-ordination of the behaviour of other members of the species (the young, and the flock and family companions), mostly in situations which are not primarily sexual but rather concerned with maintenance activities—feeding, flocking, migration and responses to predators. In those birds which are not song birds and have no song in the ordinary meaning of the term, obviously the signals used in reproductive behaviour must—if vocal at all—be of the nature of call-notes: that is, acoustically simple, and not the complex affairs we normally call song. In many waders, for instance, we get territorial-defence calls, aggressive calls, and calls serving to distinguish the mate from other members of the species; and in all these instances one may say that the call-note is serving the function which the song has assumed in the case of the oscines. But even in the song birds we can find a very large number of examples of call-notes which do on occasion, or in some species perhaps habitually, subserve a similar function to song. Examples of this are to be found in the aggressive calls of the Chaffinch (Marler, 1957) and the Blackbird (Snow, 1958), the pleasure calls of many birds, the territorial-defence calls of the Chaffinch (Poulsen, 1958, Table, p. 101), and the nest calls of the doves; so even on functional grounds we cannot make a hard and fast distinction between call-notes and song. Not infrequently, as in the Great Tit (Hinde, 1952, p. 68), a succession of call-notes may merge into song, and call-notes play an important part as constituents of song, for example, Chaffinch (Thorpe, 1958a). Other examples of this will be discussed in the next chapter. Nevertheless, the distinction between call-notes and song remains a useful one and in this chapter it is proposed to consider call-notes, as the phrase is normally understood,

16

comprising both the utterances of non-song birds and the song birds proper.

Functionally, call-notes can generally be included in one or more of the following categories:

(1) Pleasure calls;
(2) distress calls;
(3) territorial-defence calls;
(4) flight calls;
(5) feeding-calls;
(6) nest calls;
(7) flock calls;
(8) aggressive calls;
(9) general alarm calls;
(10) specialised alarm calls, such as the ground predator call and the flying predator call.

We will start by taking some characteristic examples of each of these.

First let us consider calls made only, or characteristically, by young birds, starting with *pleasure calls*. These are typical of the young of a few nidifugous birds; for, with some possible exceptions to be discussed below, pleasure calling would be obviously dysgenic when the youngsters are crowded together in a nest which is in a vulnerable situation. The domestic chick is the only species in which pleasure calling has been at all carefully investigated. This pleasure note or twittering consists of a simple musical figure repeated sometimes fairly regularly, a little faster than four times a second; more often, however, it is irregular, with no very marked rhythm and a good deal of variation. Each note lasts about a twelfth of a second, so that the chick is silent two-thirds of the time (Collias and Joos, 1953). All observers agree that the sound appears cheerful and contented to the human ear, and this is explicable when we examine its sound spectrogram (fig. 6) since it is characterised by a simple rising pitch. If transferred to musical notation, the pitch ranges from just below G up to C in the topmost octave of the piano. Although it is generally agreed that notes of this kind are not unreasonably called pleasure notes, the correlation with a pleasant situation is only of the vaguest. Chicks tend to give these notes generally in the presence of other chicks and in the absence of obviously harmful or alarming stimuli. Kaufman (personal communication) finds the utterances quite unpredictable and there is little or no evidence of any communicatory function. Some young gulls have calls not unlike that of the chick. Thus Tinbergen (1953) describes how young Herring Gulls, while still in the egg, will utter a faint squeaking note. After hatching, this note seems at first to have no particular signal function but it rapidly develops into the begging note and is used as such not merely throughout the nestling life of the chick but by females begging for food in front of males, and by both sexes prior to coition.

There are examples of nidicolous birds the young of which call persistently and for long periods while still in the nest, without their calls appearing to have any signal function. This is particularly the case in the Green Woodpecker and the Greater

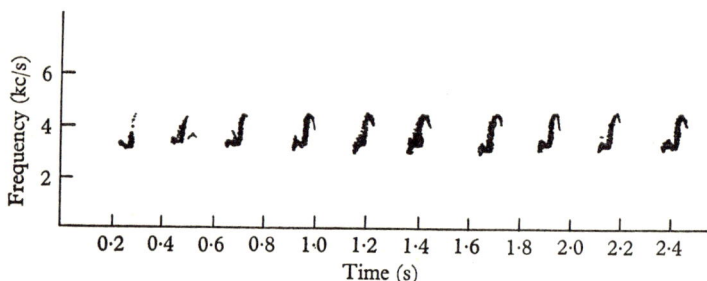

Fig. 6. Pleasure notes of 3-day-old chick of the domestic fowl.
(Collias and Joos, 1953.)

and Lesser Spotted Woodpeckers; it is also true of the Wryneck and to some extent of the Kingfisher, and field naturalists will know that the persistent high-pitched calls of the young of these species often provide the surest clue to the whereabouts of the nest hole. But it is, I think, significant that all these species are hole-nesters—consequently the young are well protected from predators and there is no grave danger in giving away the nest location. It seems probable, therefore, that pleasure calling, if this is what it is, is allowable in these species whereas it has been suppressed as dysgenic in the general run of the more vulnerable passerines. It is not difficult to find calls which can be regarded as transitional between pleasure calls and the *begging-calls* of passerines and so many other species shortly before feeding by the adult or when they have evidence of the imminent return of the parent birds. In some passerine groups, for example, the buntings (Emberizidae) (Andrew, 1957 *b*) it is possible to distinguish between close begging-calls which are uttered only when the parent bird is in the immediate neighbourhood and more distant begging-calls which are uttered for the first time when the young are about to leave the nest. During the fledgling period these calls are uttered rather infrequently by a fledgling perched alone, presumably as a guide to the return of the parent. Such distant begging-calls may be given much more frequently as the parent approaches, or may change into the close begging-call. The close begging-call is often given when the parent is actually in sight. In the American Robin, *Turdus migratorius*, this is the case, but it has been found that the bird quickly learns to recognise a human foster-parent and gives its food call readily in response to the sight of him. The parent Robin gives a food call which stimulates the begging of the chicks. When the chick actually sees the food coming it gives anticipatory calls which possibly have a close relation to pleasure calls.

There is no doubt that begging-calls of one kind and another are extremely general in the passerines; almost every careful study of passerine biology will be found to have some reference to them. They do not seem to have any very constant acoustic characteristics other than those which will be discussed below in connection with the conflicting requirements of location and concealment. However, in the Yellow Bunting, the close begging-call appears to have some of the characteristics of a pleasure call and in the buntings in general the sound spectrograms provided by Andrew (1957 *b*) do seem to show that the close begging-calls are on the whole of higher frequency and more restricted frequency range than the distant begging-calls which tend to be short, staccato and with a very wide frequency spectrum. Tinbergen (1939) found that in the Snow Bunting the nestlings have a long, high begging-call and an individual duration of 0·2 to 0·3 s would seem to be not unusual.

Next we come to the *distress call*. This seems to be more predictable than the pleasure call. In the domestic chick it is a simple *cheep* made up of descending frequencies, repeated regularly but at a much slower rate than the pleasure notes. As fig. 7 shows, it consists of a downward glide from about 5000 to 2000 cycles, thus including both higher and lower frequencies than are found in the pleasure call. Such distress calls generally appear to be evoked by unfavourable situations—cold, isolation, hunger and so forth—and what Lorenz has called 'the peeping of loneliness' in young Anatidae is presumably similar. The young Herring-Gull chick has a distress call which resembles the *ha-ha-ha* call of the adult gull. In the chick, therefore, the distress call is more predictable than is the pleasure call, but even so there are a number of anomalies. The distress call appears to be evoked by any change and also seems to be without effect on other chicks of the same age who may be completely oblivious of it. There is, however, evidence (Collias and Joos and others) that it has high value in releasing maternal behaviour on the part of the hen. There seems little doubt that the distress call of the species such as we have been considering is similar in origin to the close begging-call of passerines.

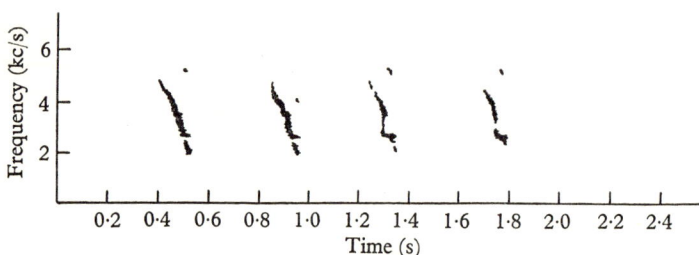

Fig. 7. Distress call of 3-day-old chick of the domestic fowl. (Collias and Joos, 1953.)

One of the most remarkable features of these two types of call is the fact that the pleasure calls immediately strike us as cheerful or encouraging, whereas the distress calls are mournful to our ears. This seems to be an instance of a very fundamental characteristic of auditory communication that applies equally to both birds and mammals, including man—namely that fairly shrill sounds which rise in pitch and have a fairly restricted lower and higher frequency (thus giving a roughly asymptotic curve on the sound spectrogram) strike us as encouraging, reassuring or cheerful; and sounds which descend over a considerable frequency range strike us as mournful, sad or pathetic. The same applies, of course, to visual design-patterns: designs or pictures having lines which curve upwards or rise to a plateau tend to be 'cheerful', those with descending lines mournful or full of foreboding. Obviously this has some relation to the human visual expression, the up-curve of the corners of

20

the mouth being cheerful and the down-curves mournful. It seems likely that the human expression may have arisen from the general significance of a rising or falling level, since raising of the corners of the mouth and the ears is in many mammals expressive of cheerfulness or expectation, and a corresponding drooping implies the reverse. This of course has already been commented upon by Darwin in his *Expression of the Emotions in Man and Animals* (1872). It is also noteworthy that both birds and mammals 'growl' over their food. This applies to many species, for example, Paridae (chickadees) and Yellow-headed Blackbirds, and it is said that the food-defence call is always the lowest-pitched of all the sounds a species makes.

A great many birds will give a fear note consisting sometimes of a short squeal, sometimes of a fear trill. This is usually characteristic of extreme anxiety, as when a bird is held in the hand. The fear trill (fig. 8) as given by a two-week-old chick consists of about five humps, the pulsations being connected. One often finds that, besides being an alarm call, the fear call may be given when squatting down, even if not alarmed, and this suggests that there may be an association between crouching for cover and the giving of alarm calls in response to a predator. The full squeal of fear does not need much comment. It often appears to be simply the expression of overwhelming emotion, but no doubt it has an important signal function in many instances since it has been part of the lore of bird snarers from time immemorial that distress squeals of birds held in the hand (particularly young birds) will have a very strong attractive effect on members of the same and sometimes of other species. Presumably in the wild this would often have the effect of attracting birds to mob a predator and so would perhaps provide the captive with a chance to escape. These squeals of fear may be uttered both by young birds and by adults. Their efficiency in releasing mobbing is very obvious in the Blackbird (Snow, 1958). The capture of Jays as a sport in France during the autumn is carried out exclusively by the use of acoustic signals (Ridpath, 1959). In this case it is the call-note of the predator itself, for example, of a buzzard or an owl, which is used to attract the Jays to mob. Mobbing trees are first carefully prepared with traps and it is said to be possible by this means to catch forty birds on one tree. Giban and Gramet (quoted by Ridpath) have shown a clear-cut positive response by winter flocks of corvids to the reproduction of the distress call of the species on loudspeakers.

The alarm call proper does not, of course, usually result in the aggregation of a species, but rather of its dispersal. It has, however, been shown that, as in the Herring Gull, an alarm

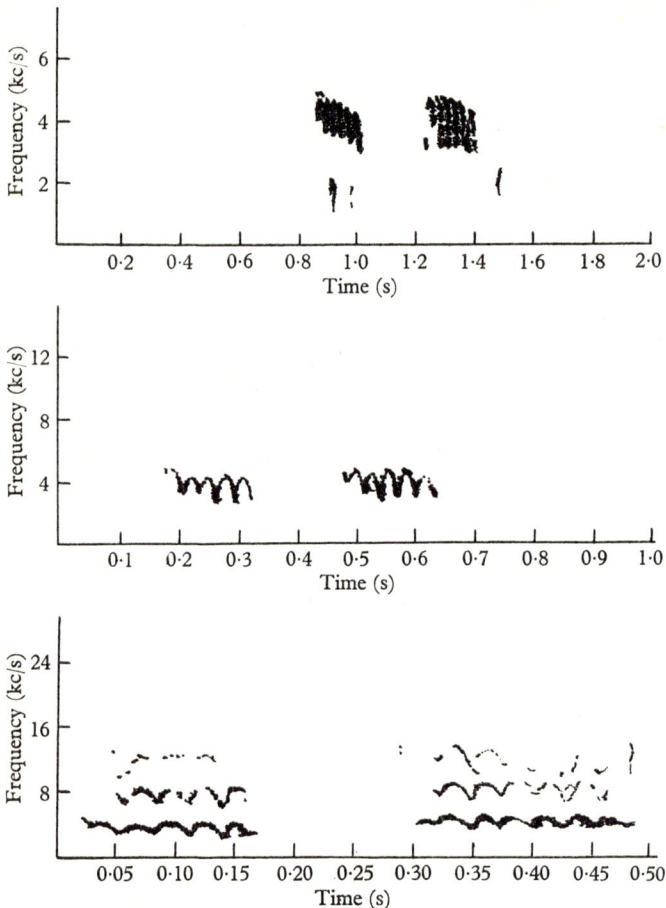

Fig. 8. Fear trills of chick of the domestic fowl. (Collias and Joos, 1953.)

call may contain both an attention component which may result first in aggregation, and an alarm component which subsequently causes dispersal. The first consists of two notes, in a descending sequence, given very sharply, and the second (the alarm call proper) consists of two more, or sometimes three, repeated staccato single notes with a major accent on the first of each series. To quote Frings, Frings, Cox and Pissner (1955) 'at the first notes of the attention call gulls rise from their places of rest and fly towards the place from which the call arises. As the alarm call proper is given, they slowly fly away. Only one sequence of the call, consisting of the attention call and two or three repetitions of the alarm call, will bring this about. In silence, the gulls circle slowly higher and higher and finally out of sight.' The use of both distress and alarm calls for acoustic scaring of birds has been tried on quite a large scale, but the results have been conflicting. Sometimes, as with Starlings, the amplification of the distress calls will have a marked effect in securing the dispersal of a starling roost, but it may have to be done at high intensity from a number of sites in the general area if it is to be relied upon. The use of alarm calls for acoustic scaring has also given some-what uncertain results hitherto. This is not to be wondered at in view of the facts just given of the two components that may exist in a normal alarm call; and also, of course, very great differences in effect may be expected with variations in the intensity and location and standard of reproduction of the recorded call. Some of the difficulties and disappointments inherent in acoustic bird scaring may become resolved as the result of more critical acoustic studies such as are described below in connection with the specific predator calls of some species.

Another problem is posed by the interspecificity of calls. In Pennsylvania there are two subspecies of the American Crow, one of which occurs there in the winter and the other in the summer, both being migrants. The winter-dwelling subspecies was not found to react to broadcast distress calls of the European Carrion Crow, whereas the subspecies which lived there in the summer did so. The reason for this difference is sought in the fact that the summer resident migrates in winter to an area where it comes into contact with several other species of crow to whose alarm signals it has learnt to react, whereas the winter subspecies, in spite of its migrations, never comes into contact with other species. The call of the American Herring Gull is said to be ineffective on Herring Gulls in Holland, whereas Busnel (quoted by Ridpath) found that the American call was effective on Herring Gulls in France. The call of the Herring Gull was found to be effective at Schipol airfield in Holland, not only on the Herring Gull, but also on the closely related Lesser

23

Black-backed Gull and the Common Gull. I understand that a permanent installation of loudspeakers to broadcast distress calls of gulls is being arranged at Schipol in order to avoid damage to planes resulting from collisions with gulls.

Food calls or feeding-calls in the strict sense—that is to say, food-finding calls—are probably rather unusual since it will only be desirable to attract a large number of individuals of a species to a particular food source from over a wide area when that food source is both abundant and ephemeral. It does, however, occur in the gulls and the food-finding call is undoubtedly an important element in the Herring Gull's vocabulary. It is emitted when gulls see food, particularly if other individuals are already present and if there is food in some quantity. Frings notes that small quantities of food discovered by one gull will usually be consumed without vocal announcements, while large quantities will elicit the call. It is stated that the food-finding call of the Herring Gull will attract individuals from up to 3 to 5 km. With small species subject to predation, the possession of a food-finding call might be dysgenic, as Miller (1952) has pointed out. With species which feed in winter flocks, the existence of food-finding or feeding-calls would not in any case be easy to establish as distinct from the presence of flock co-ordination calls, flight calls, etc.

Flock-integration calls or flight calls are, of course, of almost universal occurrence in birds which flock at any stage of their life-cycle. The phenomenon has been particularly well studied by Hinde (1952) in the Great Tit and others of the same genus. The *twink* call of this species precedes flying away and is undoubtedly in part a releaser for flight. The gentle *chich ich ich* call, on the contrary, is a call which seems to suppress flying away. It was usually found to precede a resumption of previous activity. In all cases the *twink* is associated with movement and the *chich ich ich* with cessation of movement or with staying in the same place. During the slow drifting movements of flocks through the trees, contact notes in the form of thin *tsit* or *tseet* flight notes are used and are a regular concomitant of flock-movements of all kinds. Integrated movements are accompanied by two calls, the *twink* which may be uttered in phrases of up to five notes, and the above-mentioned *chich ich ich* call. The importance of *twink* calls in the flock-organisation of the Great Tit is clearly hown by the seasonal amount of this calling (Hinde, 1952). *Twink* calls were found practically to cease in the afternoons of July and August, but this is not because other methods of co-ordination are used but because owing to the summer moult almost all co-ordinated movements stopped during that period. Sometimes the two calls are combined into a single phrase and then either may be used at the beginning or end of a movement, or when the birds settle on intermediate perches. The *twink* is used mostly in closely integrated long-range movements and occurs more at the beginning of the movement than at the end. The *chich ich ich* occurs more in loosely integrated movements and is heard much more often at the end than at the beginning. Similarly, Andrew (1957*b*) finds that many species of buntings have a flight call which can be roughly represented by the word *tit*. It may be single or may consist of three or more bursts of notes of the *tit* type, as in the rattle of the Lapland Bunting. In the Chaffinch (Marler, 1956), the *tupe* call is always associated with a flight-tendency and is one of the factors bringing about the mood for sustained flight. It can have this effect alone, although in the Chaffinch the visual sense is the most important in maintaining flock co-ordination. In small groups the *tupe* call is used freely and is thought to keep the flock together when loosely integrated, but it is rarely given by flocks of more than about fifty birds; above this size, flocks seem to be co-ordinated almost entirely by sight.

With many birds, as with mammals, a puzzling feature is the extreme variability of many of the calls. In the Great Tit, all gradations between *twink* and *tseet* flight notes on the one hand, or song on the other, may be heard. And there is reason to think that this variability is found as strongly developed in many other species of birds of similar habits and social organisation. Also there is no doubt that many bird calls vary in meaning according to their context. This may even be true of geese, where the honking of the Canada Goose displays a puzzling range of variation and of utilisation (Collias and Jahn, 1959). It seems, then, that by no means all bird calls—although they may be generally based on innate co-ordination and to that extent may be said to be innately determined—are innately fixed as to their meaning. It would thus appear that there is considerable scope for learning in the interpretation of the calls, and this is also implied by the extent to which mixed flocks of birds will respond to the calls of other species. While there is no particular difficulty in supposing that learning plays a considerable part in the development of the appropriate responses to calls[1], there would seem in many cases to be insufficient opportunity in a bird's lifetime for it to learn the correct response. However, our ignorance of the reward and reinforcement conditions operating in the formation and development of flocks is as yet so great that it is probably unwise to be dogmatic on this point. Turnstones normally respond specifically to the alarm call of the species; but Bergman (1946) found that Turnstone chicks reared under Redshanks did not respond to the notes of their own species but did so to those of their foster-parents. Nice (1943) points out that many species have both characteristic flight notes and visual flying-in-pursuit releasers consisting of a white bar at the base of the tail or elsewhere, and the regular association of the call in its various forms with the visual releaser might provide a situation where very rapid learning could occur.

A warning of the danger of going beyond the evidence as to the biological significance and necessity of alarm calls is provided by the work of Hüchtker and Schwartzkopff (1958) with operatively deafened Bullfinches. It was found that although acoustic stimuli play an important part in the attraction of a single bird by a calling fellow and in the social contacts and co-ordination of behaviour between parent and young, all the rest of the breeding-cycle, including pair formation and nest-building, proceeded normally in deaf birds in captivity. Even states of alarm could apparently be communicated perfectly by visual signals alone; but it must be borne in mind that captive birds are always close together so that visual signals may be much more effective than in the wild.

Variation in intensity and quality of alarm calls such as the *chink* call of the Chaffinch, which are not specifically a flying-up call, are of course easier to understand than are some of the examples given above, since flight will occur in an almost infinite range of intensities, and it is natural that the various intensities of the call concerned should be learnt as this range of intensities is experienced.

A problem is raised by certain passerine call-notes which, while undoubtedly appearing to be expressive of fear or a tendency to flee in certain situations, are nevertheless used very

[1] The learning of *individual* vocal differences by birds is discussed on p. 47.

much more widely—sometimes in circumstances where there seems to be no particular element of fear. An example is the *chink* call of the Chaffinch, where the motivation appears to be so complex that at least one of its variants must be presumed to be dependent on the presence of 'some sort of conflict' (Marler, 1956). Sauer (1954, 1955) treats the call *tschid* of the Whitethroat (which occurs in conflicts between tendencies to beg and to flee, to attack and to flee, or to court and to flee) as a general displacement activity. As Andrew points out, if this is so, we have here a behaviour-pattern which occurs in conflicts between a wide variety of tendencies but which, unlike the ordinary concept of displacement activity, has no autochthonous occurrences at all. A particularly interesting situation is found in those birds which have two or more calls depending upon the simultaneous presence of tendencies to fly and to give fear responses. The low-intensity calls tend to occur as flight or contact calls, and the high-intensity calls as mobbing-calls. Examples of this are found in the Great Tit (Hinde, 1952) and the Yellow Bunting (Andrew, 1957 *a*, *b*), but the best example is supplied by Andrew's work on the Blackbird (1961). Blackbirds mobbing an owl use two notes, *duck* and *tix*, which are of low and high intensity respectively. The notes are given in bouts, coinciding with flights. Calling rate increases at take-off and remains high in flight; bouts can be extended experimentally by increasing the distance the bird has to fly. Calling is slower before slow inhibited flight and accelerates more abruptly at take-off. Very short flights do not accelerate calling at take-off to the same extent. These and other lines of evidence suggest that during mobbing, the calling motivation is in some way coupled to flight motivation. The changes from low- to high-intensity notes depend on the level of excitation of calling. All the very varied types of calling can be explained in terms of an intermittent excitatory effect for flight and an instantaneous *reduction* of the general excitation level for calling (by the performance of each note) to below the threshold for the low-intensity note. Coupled with this is a much slower *increase* in inhibition during a bout of calling. Inhibition level within the 'centre' concerned acts as a minimal threshold which may vary from below the low-intensity note threshold to above that of the high-intensity note, and both inhibition and excitation decay between bouts (see fig. 9).

The fact that birds of one species will respond appropriately to the alarm calls of another species does not of course imply that this is entirely a matter of learning from experience, for it has long been known to naturalists that the alarm calls of two or more species of birds may be extraordinarily similar even though the species themselves are by no means closely related. In other words, there is to some extent a common language.

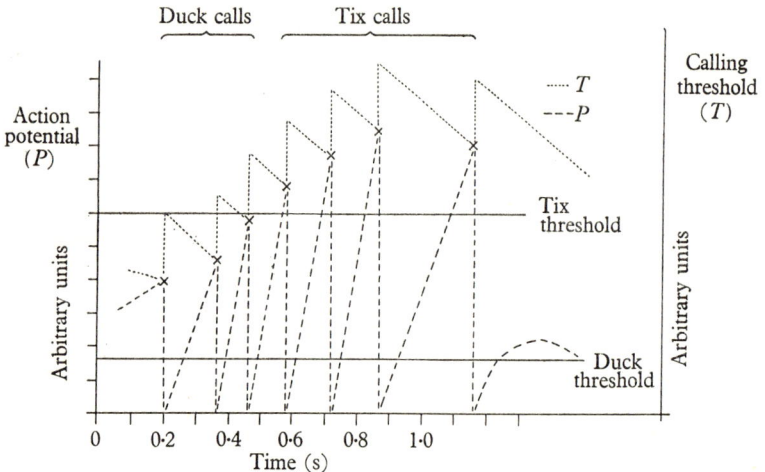

Fig. 9. Calling motivation. A bout of calls of the Blackbird given when perched. The increase of T during the calling-bout is here arbitrarily represented as the result of a fixed increment at each call, followed by decay at a standard rate between calls. The factors tending to increase P are high during the bout and low or absent at beginning or end. This is represented here by a slow rate of recovery of P at the beginning and end of the bouts; after the final call P begins to rise and then decays when the factors tending to increase it cease to be active. The points at which P reaches the value of T are marked with crosses and represent the beginning of a call. (Andrew, 1961.)

Thus the call which a male Blackbird gives in response to a hawk in flight is scarcely distinguishable from that given by a Chaffinch. So many examples are now known of species which have two quite different alarm calls, one for a predator in flight and another for a predator on the ground or perched in a tree, that it is clear that some rather fundamental principles must be involved in the evolution of these characteristics. This has been particularly studied in the Chaffinch and some other species by Marler (1956). The accuracy of sound-location depends on the capabilities of the auditory receptors of the animal concerned, upon the physical characteristics of the sound-signal itself and on the distinctiveness of the sound, including the effects of distance from the source and of contrast as against various noises in the environment. Man has of course been far more extensively studied in this respect than any other animal (an excellent account will be found in Stevens and Davis, 1938) but there are a considerable number of experiments on other mammals and also on birds. In both groups sounds are located by the making of binaural comparisons of differences in phase, intensity and time of arrival of the sounds. In contrast with insects, which have a very different method of hearing, the efficiency with which the sound can be located varies with the frequency of the signal. Phase difference can be employed for sound location when the crest of one sound wave reaches the further receptor before the crest of a second wave reaches the nearer. It is most useful at low frequencies because the information it provides becomes ambiguous when the wavelength is less, or much less, than twice the distance between the ears. It is conceivable that the refractory period of the auditory nerve, which is 1 ms, limits the perception of phase difference to frequencies less than 1 kc/s—that is, 1 c/ms. Intensity differences provide quite a valuable method of sound-location, but they are most useful at high frequencies since obstructions in the path of the sound will only cast appreciable sound-shadow when the dimensions of the obstructing object are greater than the wavelength of the signal. The head of the hearer is, of course, the main cause of sound-shadow. Appreciation of the gross difference in time of arrival of the sound at the two ears can, however, be used throughout the auditory range and Marler points out that the most readily located signals will be those which provide clues for all three methods. As we shall see in a later chapter, the song of the Chaffinch, and indeed of a great many other small passerines also, is such that many and varied clues for direction are offered to the hearer and the physical characteristics of the songs of many other small birds are closely adapted to the part the song plays in the life. Thus they will contain phrases made up of notes frequently repeated and of brief duration, and also containing relatively low frequencies. The same applies to the clucking sounds with which the domestic fowl attracts small chicks and in this case the frequencies include sounds lower than 800 c/s. Much of the energy is concentrated at the start of the note and in both Chaffinch song and the clucking of the domestic fowl the sounds are such as to allow both phase differences and time differences to be used for location.

In the case of sounds which give warning of the approach or presence of predators, two distinct and conflicting tendencies appear in the vocalisations as they do in the coloration of the animal. These are the need to appear conspicuous to their own species and the conflicting need to appear inconspicuous to predators or prey. This appears to be the prime reason why so many small passerines have two distinct responses to a hawk or

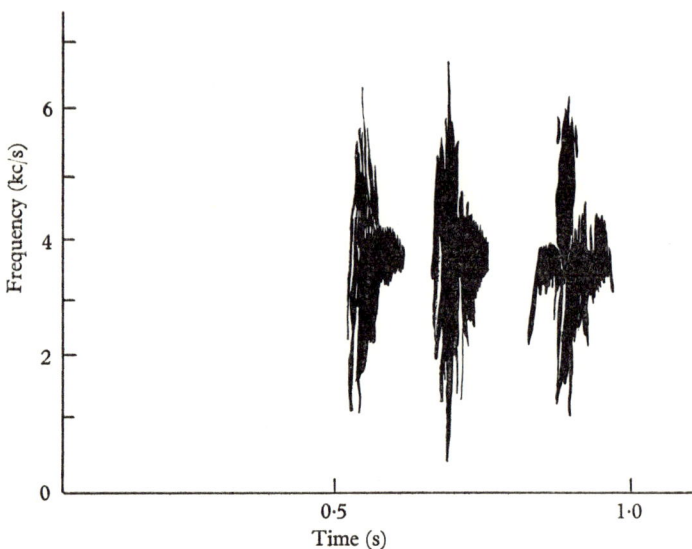

Fig. 10. Chaffinch. *Chink* call. (Thorpe, 1958*a*.)

to an owl. If the bird of prey is perched they tend to make themselves conspicuous by mobbing behaviour which attracts attention to the predator; if it is in flight, they dash for cover and hide. Finches tend to use quite different calls in these two circumstances.[1] In the first, the Chaffinch, for instance, gives a *chink* note (fig. 10) which provides abundant location clues; in the second the males give a high thin *seeet* note (fig. 11). The first—the *chink* call—is easily located by man, the second only with difficulty; and it is a reasonable assumption that the same is true for predators. Pure tones of about 2–5 kc/s are hard for

[1] Collias (1960) describes a similar situation in the domestic fowl.

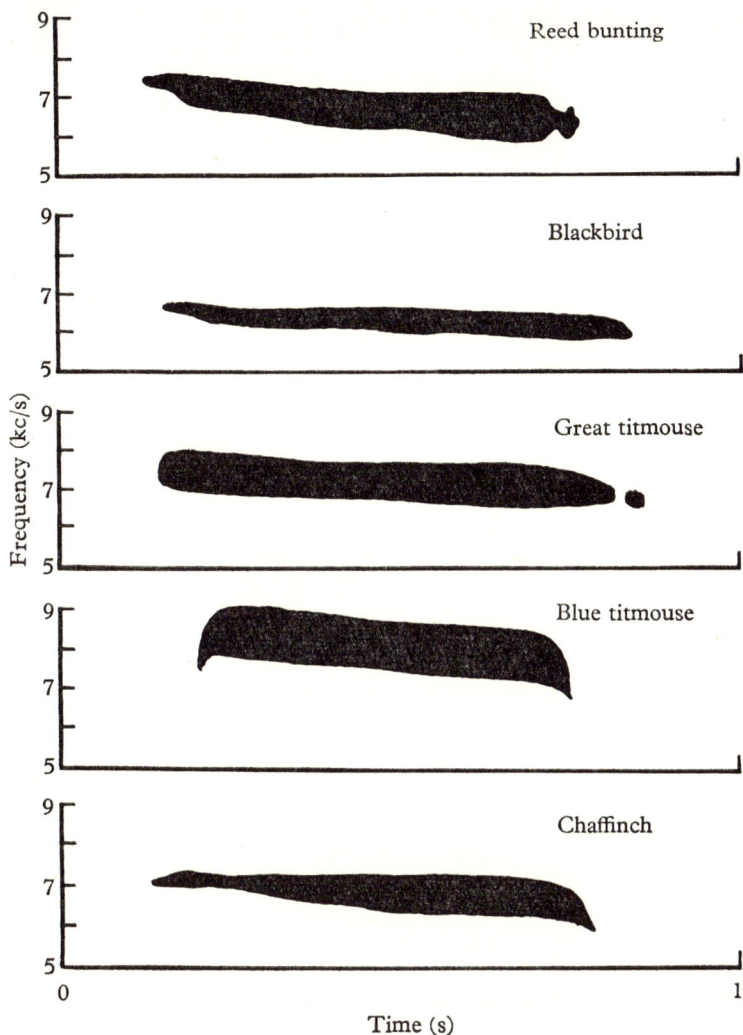

Fig. 11. The calls of five different species given when a hawk
flies over. (Marler, 1959.)

man to locate because they are too high for binaural comparison
of phase difference and too low for there to be appreciable
intensity differences, so that only time differences can be
employed. Marler points out that in birds of prey such as owls
and hawks the lower limit of this range of frequencies is probably

similar to that of man; this may have some relation to the refractory period above-mentioned, but the upper limit must be considerably higher since sound-shadows only become appreciable when the wavelength approximates to the diameter of the obstruction. Thus the *seeet* call of the male Chaffinch and the hawk calls of many other birds are such as to give few or no clues to location by phase- or intensity-differences. Moreover, these calls usually begin and end imperceptibly and thus also fail to give clues for comparison of binaural time differences. Further, the wavelength is small enough to result in free reflection from trunks and branches of trees so that it seems as if the *seeet* call is adjusted to avoid giving locational clues to any kind of predator. Yet it serves to communicate the presence of danger to other Chaffinches which, upon hearing it, fly to the nearest cover irrespective of the location of the calling bird.[1]

When we look at the food begging-call of young birds from this point of view the picture is not entirely clear, but it is certainly true that newly fledged young birds which are, of course, extremely vulnerable to attack, do not normally give calls which are audible at a very great distance and frequently their calls are more similar to the hawk call of a Blackbird or a Chaffinch than to the alarm calls of adults of their own species. Thus the food begging-call of the young Wren is extremely difficult to locate. Fig. 11 shows the flying-predator alarm call of five different species of passerine birds belonging to different subfamilies (Marler, 1959). When, however, the object of a call is to attract the attention of other members of the species and

[1] Voipio (1952) describes how a young Green Sandpiper taken in the hand was heard to emit sounds of very high pitch, approaching the upper limit of sound audible to the human ear. Although this sound was audible to human beings, only when the bird was held close to the ear, the parent reacted to it instantaneously from a distance of at least 50 m. The cries emitted by the young one made the mother swoop to the spot. It is suggested that the significance of a high-pitched call for warning communication may be that it is inaudible to an enemy moving along the ground or—if audible—is so high-pitched for certain species that the placing of its direction is difficult. As the mother, however, can divine precisely the point of origin of the sound, she can at the critical moment be immediately on the spot and draw the enemy's attention to herself. Voipio, however, does not explain how the parent bird (if she does not know the position of the offspring already) is able to localise the high-pitched sound which one would have thought would have been hard to locate whatever the aural equipment of the bird might be.

of other species to the presence of a perched predator such as an owl, the type of call used is entirely different. Fig. 12 shows the owl-mobbing calls of seven different species of birds (Marler, 1959). It would be desirable, however, that such calls should have a certain degree of specific distinctiveness and indeed they probably have been selected for a moderate degree of specificity. This may concern tempo and pitch rather than note-form, as fig. 13 will show (Marler, 1957). The alarm and food-finding calls of the Herring Gull have already been referred to, and

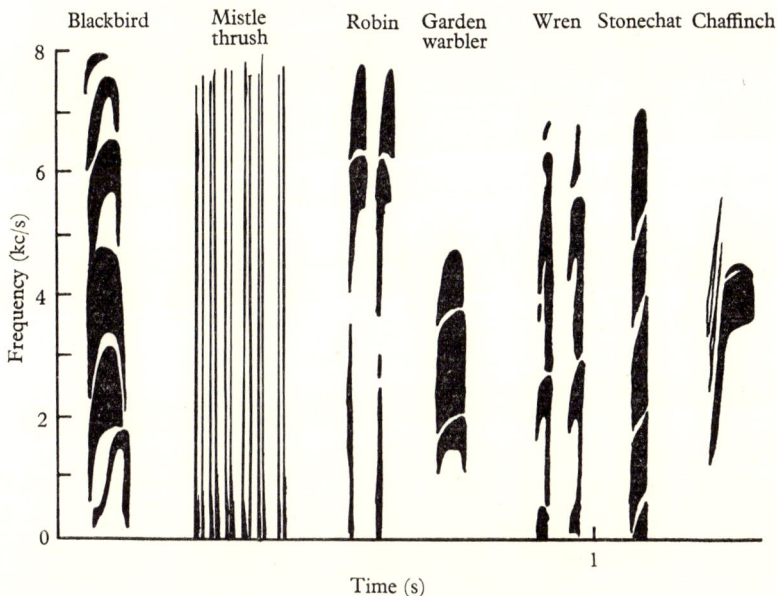

Fig. 12. Calls of birds from several families given while mobbing an owl. (Marler, 1959.)

there is no doubt that the same phenomenon of interspecific similarity of alarm and food-finding calls obtains on the sea-shore and open sea as it does in the woods and fields which the finches inhabit. Thus the Lesser Black-backed shares to some extent a common language with the Herring Gull. The mutual advantage of similar alarm calls is obvious and it may apply where the food supply is not limited so that the species do not compete. As Armstrong (1946) has pointed out, interspecific communication may be one of the most efficient ways of keeping track of fish shoals and be of mutual value to all concerned.

It is probable that the majority of species of birds possess a specific aggressive call, but in not many instances has the matter been carefully investigated. In the buntings, Andrew (1957a) found that eight of the ten species investigated have an aggressive call of the *chaa* or *chu* type. The *chaa* has a harsh vibrant quality and spectrographically is similar to the aggressive calls of a number of cardueline finches. The second type is given when fear is strong and seems to be related to the high-pitched *tsee* alarm call: both may be repeated to form a chattering sound. Intermediates between the two types of call have been described. The familiar persistent *chinking* of Blackbirds

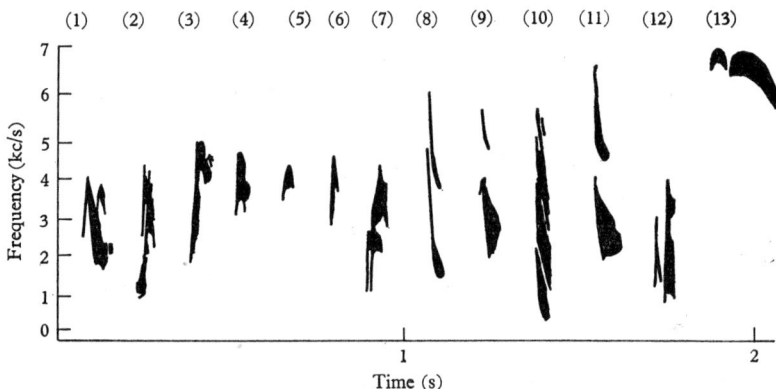

Fig. 13. Flight calls of cardueline and fringilline finches. The species shown are: (1) Redpoll, (2) Siskin, (3) Serin, (4) Oriental Greenfinch, (5) Bullfinch, (6) Goldfinch, (7) Crossbill, (8) Linnet, (9) Greenfinch, (10) Brambling, (11) Chaffinch, (12) Black-tailed Hawfinch. (Marler, 1957.)

at dusk is also apparently a territorial defence call. Snow (1958) finds that *chinking* is most intense in places where good roosting sites attract strange birds from outside the area. The resident birds chase intruders, who approach silently and furtively, but eventually they give up and allow the visitors to settle down in their roosts. In territories where roosting-sites are few, the territory-holders nevertheless usually take up a conspicuous perch and *chink* for some minutes before going to roost. Snow says 'this evening chinking thus seems to serve as an assertion of ownership at a time when territories are habitually invaded by strange birds.' The Blackbird also has an aggressive thin piercing *tsee* lasting about a second and delivered with the beak slightly open. It is rather more highly pitched than the alarm *tsee* but otherwise is very similar. It is uttered by combative and usually dominant birds in circumstances connected with the taking up and maintenance of territory. The aggressive call of the Chaffinch is rather more puzzling. Marler reports it as the individual peculiarity of a few captive males. There is an aggressive form of the *chink* which is used by practically all birds under the appropriate conditions but in addition there is a low buzzing call rendered as *zzzzzz* or *zhzhzh*, consisting of a wide band of frequencies of a fairly constant mean pitch. This call is used during attack and fighting at close quarters. It is in fact not unlike the more intense aggressive call of some of the buntings. The Wren has a variety of urgent and vituperative-sounding utterances which have been described as 'wheezy', 'squealing' and 'spitting', and which appear certainly to be aggressive in function (Armstrong, 1955). Sound spectrograms are not available but there seems little doubt that, *mutatis mutandis*, the calls are acoustically similar to those described in finches. Nice (1943) devotes much space to the study of the intimidation methods of her Song Sparrows. Here again there is an aggressive *zheee* note; but in addition she describes a note, which seems to be unique, used in aggression towards a person endangering the young. It is described as *puh, puh, puh*. Aggressive calls are not as a rule reserved for use in specific situations but rather tend to be employed under any circumstances in which aggression is to be expressed. It is therefore to be expected that aggressive calls will frequently be used in territorial defence, even though a specific song may have been evolved apparently for this very purpose. Thus Poulsen (1958) describes a territorial defence call in the Chaffinch, and the Blackbird uses its alarm *tsee* for this purpose. And of course challenge, aggressive and territorial defence calls are almost universal in birds which have not developed songs, provided they use vocalisations at all.

Finally, we come to calls particularly concerned with relations between the sexes. The Chaffinch has three different courtship calls uttered by the male and perhaps to some extent specialised for different phases in the courtship cycle. However, it seems more likely that which of these calls is employed in a given instance depends chiefly upon relative intensities of the aggressive and fear components which are always present in sex behaviour. Curio (1959) in his admirable study of the life-history and behaviour of the Pied Flycatcher (race, *hypoleuca*), describes the pattern, causation and biological significance of fifteen simple call-notes which seem to fit in well with the classification here adopted. His explanation of the variability in call-notes, which is a feature of this species as with others we have dealt with, is based on assumptions about tension caused by the simultaneous activation of two incompatible drives under a high level of excitement, and he thinks that this gives rise to some call-notes which are intermediate between two otherwise well defined types (see his fig. 16, p. 31). In many of those species of passerine birds in which a fairly complete inventory of the call-notes has been made, there seems to exist a specific nest-site call, used when looking for a nest-site, when building and when attracting a mate to the nest-site.[1] Similarly, female-soliciting calls or pre-copulation greeting calls are usual. They are often hastily repetitive, though quiet, as befits utterances serving communication between two birds which are in close proximity; they often give the impression of suppressed urgency —being, so to speak, 'congested'. There are many instances of song which, when used for communicating between two individuals of a pair at the time of mating, have this same feature of urgency, haste and 'congestion' (see Armstrong, 1955). Here again, as in territorial defence, we may guess such calls to be general in birds which communicate vocally.

It may be significant that in many cases where the vocabulary of a passerine bird has been well studied the number of 'words' in use in the form of call-notes tends to work out at about the same (Table 1). Thus Nice describes sixteen different types of call-note given by adult Song Sparrows. In the Chaffinch there are fifteen basic calls. Similarly, with the buntings, thirteen or fourteen seems to be the maximum number. Sauer (1954), on the Whitethroat, describes fourteen calls, although he gives a great many minute variants of the various flight and warning calls. Armstrong finds twelve main call-notes in the Wren. Messmer has fourteen for the Blackbird, and Curio eleven (with intermediates) for the Pied Flycatcher. It seems, then, that although the variety of calls which can be produced and presumably the variety that can be distinguished by the bird's ear, is almost infinite, there is some common factor working in all

[1] In the Great Tit tapping with the beak seems to serve instead of a nest-site call.

TABLE 1. *Number and functions of call-notes in various species*

Circumstances in which uttered	(1) Fowl	(2) Dove (vars.)	(3) Dove (Barbary)	(4) Great tit	(5) Chaffinch	(6) Buntings	(7) Blackbird	(8) Whitethroat	(9) Pied flycatcher	(10) Wren	(11) Herring gull	(12) Song sparrow
Calls of adults												
Flight	.	.	.	✳	✳	✳	✳	✳	.	.	.	✳
Settling	.	✳	.	✳	.	.	.	✳	.	.	.	.
Social (flock)	.	✳	.	✳	✳	✳	✳	✳	✳	✳	✳(2)	✳
Alarm 1	✳	✳	✳	✳	✳	✳	✳	✳	✳	✳	✳	✳
Alarm 2	.	.	.	.	✳	✳	✳	✳	✳	✳	.	✳
Alarm 3	.	.	.	.	✳	✳	✳	✳	✳	✳	.	✳
Flying predator	.	.	.	✳	✳	.	✳	.	✳	✳	.	.
Ground predator	✳	.	.	✳	✳	.	✳	?	.	✳	.	✳
Scream (injury)	✳	✳	.	.	✳	.	✳	.	✳	✳	.	✳(2)
Aggressive	✳	✳	✳	.	✳	✳	.	✳	✳	✳	✳	✳
Territorial	✳	.	.	.	.	.	✳	✳	✳	.	.	✳
Courtship 1	.	✳	✳	✳	✳	✳	✳	✳	.	✳	.	✳
Courtship 2	.	.	✳	.	✳	.	.	✳	.	✳	.	✳
Courtship 3	.	.	.	.	✳	.	.	✳	.	.	.	.
Copulation	.	✳	.	✳	✳	✳	.	✳	.	✳	✳	✳
Nest-site	.	✳	✳	.	.	✳	.	.	✳	.	.	✳
Mate feeding	.	.	.	✳	.	✳	.	?	.	.	✳	.
Food	✳	.	.	.	.	.	.	.	.	.	✳	.
Roosting	.	.	.	.	.	.	✳	?	.	✳	.	.
	6	8	5	9	13	10	11	12 (or 15)	9	12	7	14
Calls of young												
Pleasure	✳	.	.	.	.	.	.	.	.	.	.	.
Distress	✳	.	.	.	.	.	✳	✳	.	.	.	✳
Distant begging	.	.	.	.	✳	✳	✳	✳	✳	.	.	✳
Close begging	.	.	.	.	✳	✳	✳	✳	✳	✳	.	✳
	2	.	.	.	2	2	3	3	2	1	.	3
Total	8	8	5	9	15	12	14	15 (or 18)	11	13	7	17

Sources of information: (1) Collias and Joos (1953); (2) Whitman (1919); (3) Miller and Miller (1958); (4) Hinde (1952); (5) Marler (1956), Poulsen (1958); (6) Andrew (1957b); (7) Messmer and Messmer (1956), Snow (1958); (8) Sauer (1954); (9) Curio (1959); (10) Armstrong (1955); (11) Tinbergen (1953), Frings, Frings, Cox and Pissner (1955); (12) Nice (1943).

these species which limits the number of the main items of information conveyable by this means to approximately fifteen. In the Chaffinch Marler finds that, excluding song and nestling and fledgling calls, five of the notes give environmental information, nine social information, seven identifying information, and seven locating information.

CHAPTER 3

Song

SONG, in the sense of a recognisable sequence or pattern of notes of more than one kind, is of course uncommon outside the oscines, and it is primarily the song of the true song-birds with which we shall be concerned in the present chapter. Since, however, as was made clear above, the song of the song-birds can often be regarded as replacing and extending the function of certain call-notes found in the non-song birds, it will be found that some of the matters considered in the present chapter overlap those discussed in the previous one.

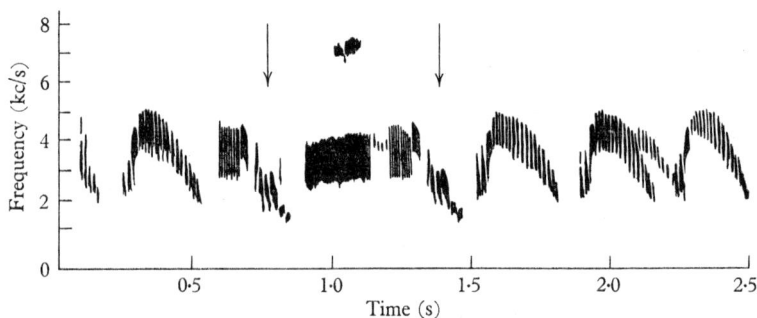

Fig. 14. Skylark. Typical sequences of song containing flight-call components, indicated by arrows.

The relation between call-notes and song is often very evident. Howard (1920) refers to a number of cases in which a particular call-note is uttered with unusual energy during sexual emotion and is attached to the song or may actually be said to form a part of it. He points out that a still closer connection can be found in species having relatively simple songs, where these are seen to be merely compositions of social and family calls repeated many times in succession. This is particularly the case in some of the pipits and to some extent also in the Skylark (see fig. 14) where the alarm call or flight call constitutes a major component of the song. Of course in species

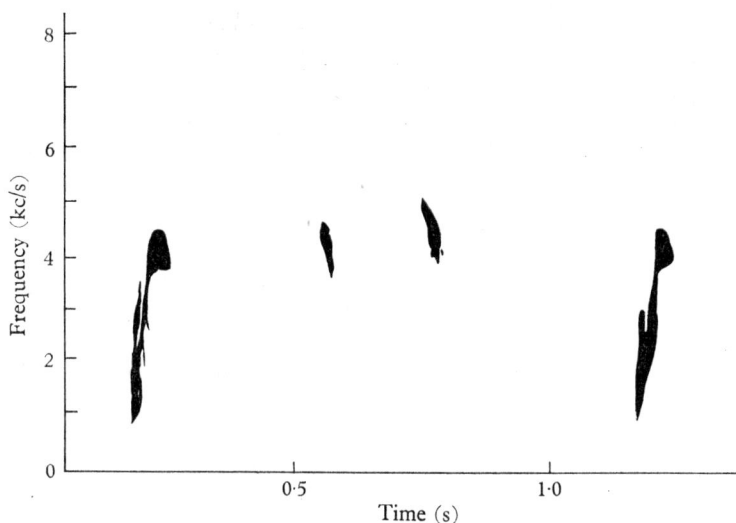

Fig. 15. Chaffinch. The soft *chink* call, an alarm note of medium intensity. (Thorpe, 1958a.)

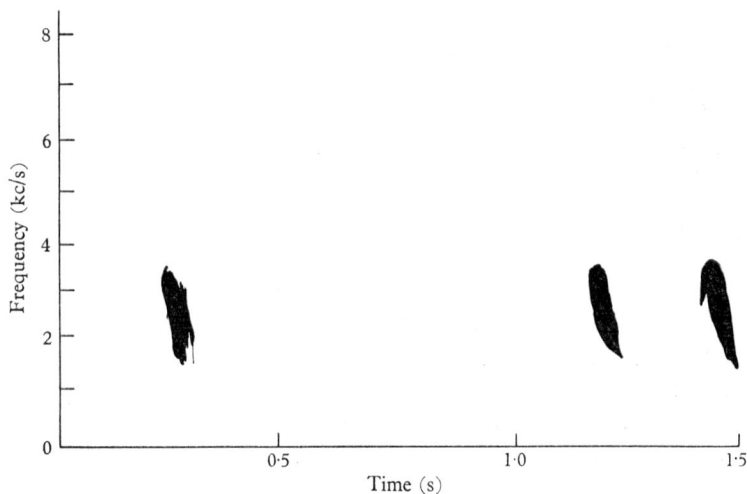

Fig. 16. Chaffinch. The *tupe* note, a flight call. (Thorpe, 1958a.)

with a somewhat restricted vocal repertoire, lacking in variety of tone colour, the notes of the song are to some extent bound to resemble the call-notes. But the connection between call-notes and song is often closer than would seem to be dictated merely by the restricted capacity of the vocal organs. Howard

39

gives an interesting example of the seasonal vocal development of such a bird as the Yellow Bunting where we can observe the gradual elaboration from simple to complex, from the repetition of single notes to phrases and from phrases to the complete melody, and he concludes that we have every reason to suppose that it is along these lines that the evolution of the voice has proceeded. It is perhaps not surprising that there should be this close relation between song and call-notes in groups such as the pipits, the buntings and even the larks. But it is somewhat unexpected to find how big a part a similar process plays in birds such as the Whitethroat (Sauer, 1954). There, however, we must remember that the song, even though complex, seems to be, like the call-notes, mainly innate. In such a bird as the Chaffinch where learning plays a considerable part in the development of the full song, it is also found that the call-notes are employed in the process of building up the structure of the true song to a quite considerable degree (Thorpe, 1958a). Thus the soft *chink* (fig. 15), an alarm call of medium intensity, and the *tupe* (fig. 16), a flight call, are both to be found as components of the full song. The *huit* call, another alarm note (fig. 17), is seen as the first note of phrase 2 of the song of Chaffinch RWB/RWB/W[1] (fig. 18). Alarm notes of really high intensity are less likely, however, to be included in the song. Thus the hard *chink* of the Chaffinch is omitted from the song. If one compares the sound spectrograms of normal chaffinch song with those of the experimental groups of Kaspar Hauser birds[2] (figs. 19–20) one notices at once that call-notes tend to be more in evidence as components of the latter than of the former. This is perhaps a reflection of the restricted auditory experience of the Kaspar Hauser birds. They lack the practical experience which, it is not unreasonable to suppose, normally provides Chaffinches with additional material from which to build their songs, and these isolated birds seem consequently to make more use of the innate

[1] Such capital letters, here and elsewhere, refer to the code of colour rings by which my experimental Chaffinches were individually marked.

[2] Kaspar Hauser was a dumb, helpless and bewildered German peasant youth who appeared in mysterious circumstances in Nuremberg in 1828. It was alleged, almost certainly falsely, that he was the illegitimate son of the Grand Duke Charles of Baden and that he had been kidnapped sixteen years before and given to a peasant family who reared him in strict isolation. Although the story has been more or less discredited, the name has become a standard one for animals reared in isolation from their species.

call-notes which they all possess. But though call-notes certainly have their place in many true songs, it is probably safe to say that in general the notes of the true song are much more complex than are call-notes, and certainly in experienced and normally treated Chaffinches the notes of the true song are developed independently out of the material of the subsong (see p. 64 below).

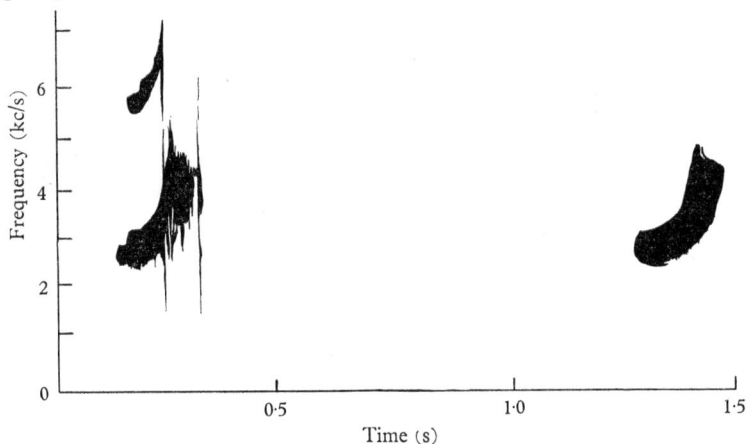

Fig. 17. Chaffinch. The *huit* note, an alarm note which may be incorporated in one or other of the early phrases of the full song. (Thorpe, 1958a.)

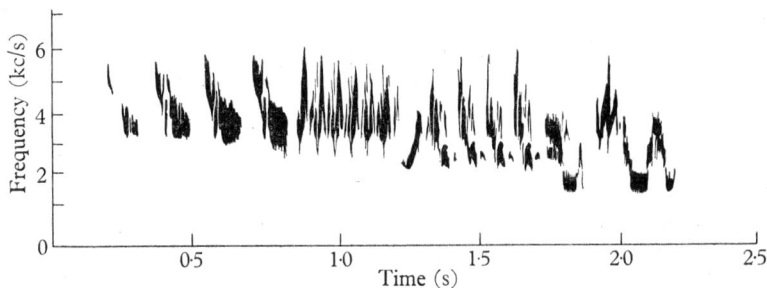

Fig. 18. Chaffinch. Full song. Note inclusion of *huit* call-note in the middle of phrase 2 of the song. (Thorpe, 1958a.)

It has always been evident to naturalists that full song is connected with the breeding-cycle, and we now know how closely related is the seasonal incidence of song to the seasonal growth of the gonads (Davis, 1958) and the consequent seasonal production of testosterone. But any theory of the biological function of song was bound to be very far short of the true mark until the territory theory came to be elaborated and its main assumptions established. Both Aristotle and Pliny seem to have observed that bird fighting was often concerned with the possession of a site; but more than sixteen hundred years were to elapse before any further mention seems to have been made in the literature. Then Olina (writing in Rome, in 1622) and

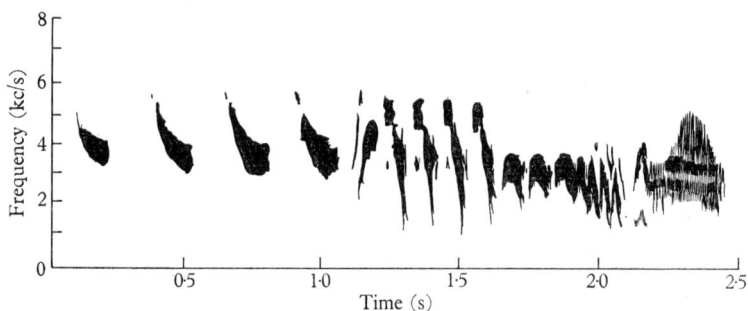

Fig. 19. Chaffinch. Full song of a bird from a Kaspar Hauser group of two. Note that the first note of phrase 2 is closely similar to the soft *chink* call-note. (Thorpe, 1958a.)

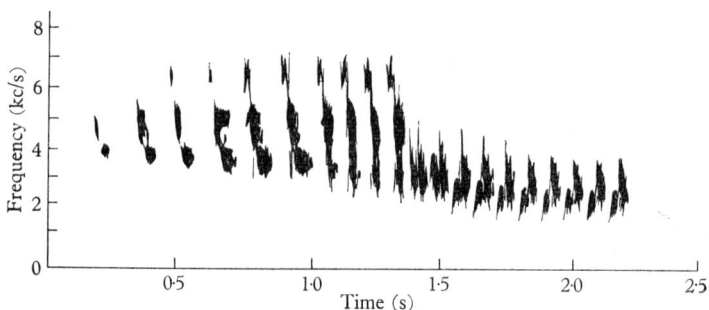

Fig. 20. Chaffinch. Full song of a member of a Kaspar Hauser group of five. Note the similarity of several of the notes to the soft *chink* call-note. (Thorpe, 1958a.)

Witherings (writing in England, in 1632) referred to breeding-birds as inhabiting a 'freehold', and Willoughby added that the Nightingale will not admit any other Nightingale to this freehold but its mate. From then on the references to territory as a defended area become more numerous, but one may say that the territory theory as such was first established by the work of Eliot Howard (1907–14), which gave rise to his book *Territory in Bird Life* (1920). From this and the writings of many other naturalists it is well established that song is often a territorial proclamation and an actual means of defence—in fact a form of substitute fighting. The male sings from a particular perch or perches within the territory. His singing thus to a large extent marks out territorial boundaries, constitutes a threat to rivals and often an advertisement to potential mates; and it is difficult to see how songs, in anything like the form in which we now know them, could have been evolved apart from these basic territorial functions. Armstrong has pointed out (1955, p. 70) that in many passerines, including the Wren, a territory which becomes silent through accident to the owner is soon invaded. Brown and Davies (1949) describe instances in which male Reed Warblers which did not respond vigorously to the singing of an unmated intruder were deserted by their mates. Observations of this kind provide good evidence for the importance of the proprietor's song in keeping a territory inviolate. There is no doubt that, considered from the acoustic point of view, the characteristic song of territorial species usually appears well adapted for this function of territorial advertisement and defence. Since the singer is trying to make himself conspicuous the song must be of a type that will carry far and give plenty of clues for location. A glance at figs. 21 and 22 will show how well the songs there depicted fulfil these requirements. It is common knowledge that two birds in adjacent territories appear to be answering one another and there is a considerable amount of observational evidence that the vigorous and oft-repeated song of a male in possession of a territory will discourage an intruding male, not yet a territory-holder, and may even put him to flight without any other form of aggressive display, let alone actual attack, having been necessary. Assuming then that, as in the Chaffinch, the song is specifically distinct and is recognisable by other members of the species as specific, the information conveyed to a potential or actual rival by a male Chaffinch newly established in the territory is (1) a Chaffinch, (2) a male, (3) within his territory, (4) in a particular place, (5) ready to make a repulsive attack on other chaffinches (see Marler, 1956). Where, as we shall see, song is not merely specifically but also individually characteristic, this information too may be transmitted. The rival may recognise a given male not merely by the position of his territory but actually by his individual voice, independently of his territory.

43

It is characteristic of the territorial singing of birds that it proceeds for long periods at very regular intervals, the utterances seeming relatively independent of external stimulation. The unmated male Chaffinch will produce its song, which is of from 2 to $2\frac{1}{2}$ s duration, at a fairly regular interval of something between 7 and 15 s. There is some evidence that the period

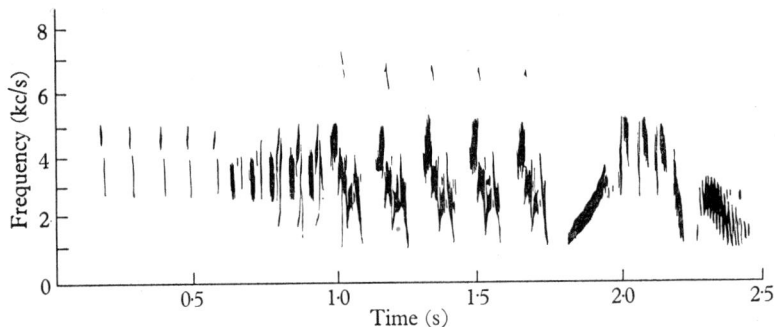

Fig. 21. Chaffinch, *Fringilla c. coelebs*, Denmark. Typical full song. (Thorpe, 1958*a*.)

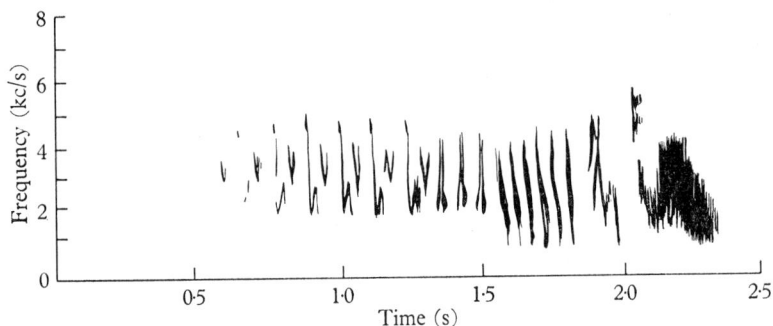

Fig. 22. Chaffinch, *Fringilla c. gengleri*. Typical full song. Madingley, Cambridge. (Thorpe, 1958*a*.)

between songs (i.e. the mean rest-period) may be greater in some geographical districts (for example, eastern England) than it is in others (for example, south-western England) (Barber, 1948, 1959). It is very usual for the unmated male to sing more frequently than does the mated male; indeed it is said that a permanently mated Brown Towhee does not sing at all (Quaintance 1938). Haartmann (1956) found that the unmated male Pied Flycatcher sings about 3600 songs per

44

day, whereas the mated male sings less than 1000. Dr von Haartmann (in preparation) has now amplified these results. He finds that song, like a number of other activities, displays a basic rhythm, by which is meant the varying frequency of the activity at different times of day, at a certain day-length under constant external influences. The basic rhythm of song-frequency of unmated males changes from the early to the late mating-season. Thus in May the song-frequency decreases considerably at 1 p.m. if not earlier, whereas in June unmated males sing until late in the evening. An example of this is shown in fig. 23. Newly mated males behave like unmated males (curve *a*) in the morning—that is, they sing loudly until the female appears, he being an earlier riser than his mate. As soon as she is on the scene, he suddenly stops singing and instead shows bouts of a number of other activities appropriate to the early stages of breeding, for example, showing the nest-site, sexual flight, copulation, courtship feeding, etc. This is shown very graphically in fig. 23 *b* where the very high song-frequency between the hours of 2 and 2.30 is not repeated during the day, after the female is awake. After a male bird has acquired a female the rhythm of the song changes as well as the total quantity and frequency of song. This depression of song activity during the time when the female is active about the territory may perhaps simply be owing to the fact that his time is taken up by many other activities directed towards the female and taking precedence over song. Again, Nice found that the Song Sparrow proclaiming territory whilst unmated would sing from 180 to 200 songs per hour, the range being from 59 to 310, whereas after mating has been achieved the maximum number of songs per hour was 160, and more often within the range of 30–50. Montagu (1802, quoted by Lack, 1943) seems to have been the first to realise that song may be a means by which the females distinguish mated from unmated males, and he was also the first to understand the importance of song as an individual recognition mark. Marler found with the Chaffinch that the male dropped his rate of singing on acquiring a mate, and he had good evidence that this difference in frequency between mated and unmated males is perceived by females seeking a mate and that accordingly they are attracted only to males with the higher rate of song. It has been observed in the Snow Bunting that even the temporary absence of a female will set the male singing once again (Tinbergen, 1939). The number of songs uttered per day by an unmated male Pied Flycatcher in the full vigour of territorial defence is remarkable enough, but

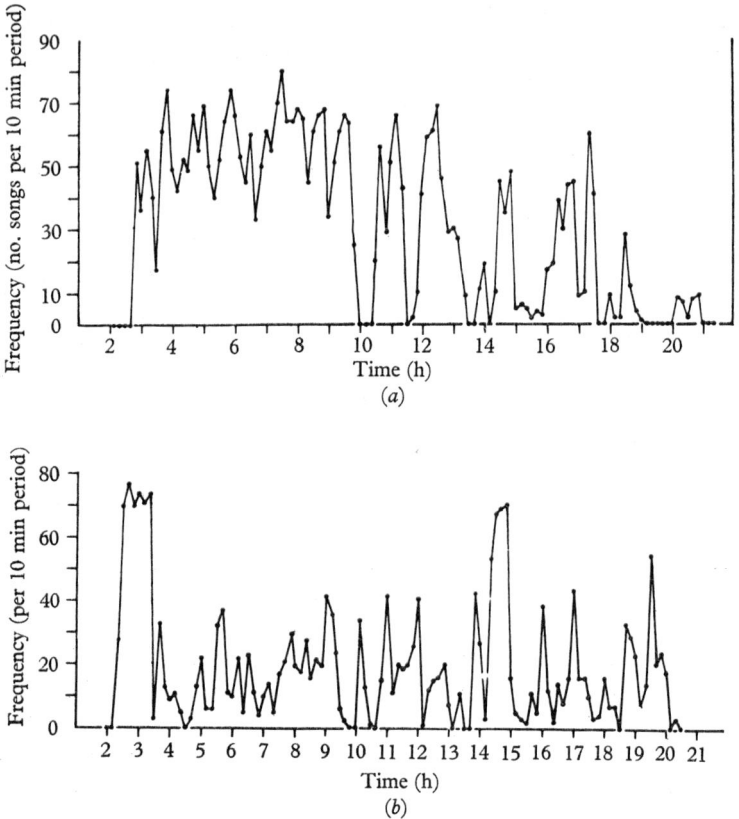

Fig. 23. The song rhythm of the Pied Flycatcher. Ordinate: number of songs per 10-min interval; abscissa: hours of the day. Curve (a), the total song performance of an unmated male during the 24 h of 3 June 1955, Tvärminne, Finland. The curve is typical of unmated males. Curve (b), song performance of a mated male during the 24 h of 1 June 1959, Tvärminne, Finland. A day in which his female was engaged in nest-building. The curve is typical of this situation. Note high frequency in early morning before the female is awake. As soon as she appears, the male is much less vocal. (von Haartmann, in the Press.)

not even this species can compare with the Red-eyed Vireo which has been recorded as uttering nearly 22,200 songs in the course of a single day (de Kiriline, 1954). No one can doubt that such stupendous activity must serve some major biological end.

As will be described below, many species have a number of different songs in their repertoire—that is to say, each bird will have songs which, while characteristic of the species, yet include individual peculiarities which render them distinct. Thus individual Chaffinches may have as many as six different songs (though this is exceptional), and individual Song Sparrows apparently generally possess from four to six songs, and exceptional birds up to twenty-four (Nice, 1943). The method of acquisition of these variations will be discussed below (pp. 74–7); it is noteworthy as providing good evidence that the birds themselves recognise and come to know these individual differences.

That birds can recognise one another individually by means of vocal characteristics is, of course, certainly not confined to song, in the strict sense. On the contrary, evidence seems to be continually accumulating that peculiarities of call-notes can be a very effective method of individual distinction. The degree to which individual birds do know one another, quite irrespective of knowing the territory, is astonishing. Examples will be found in Thorpe (1956, pp. 377–9). This recognition is based both on voice and appearance. A Herring Gull can recognise its mate in flight at 30 yards, even though it is silent, and a sleeping gull will be awakened by the long-drawn mew call of its mate although the same call uttered by any other bird leaves the sleeping bird quite unconcerned (Tinbergen, 1953). The same seems to be true of Kittiwake Gulls and of some terns. Tschanz (1959) shows that the young of the Guillemot learn to react selectively to the calls of the parent during the first few days of life, and the parents similarly recognise their young. Stonehouse (pers. comm.) describes how the 'rookeries' or 'crèches' of the King Penguin in Antarctica contain many thousands of chicks. The chicks are called out from the crèche by the parents returning with food. Apparently each chick learns the individual rhythm of its parent's call which is different from those of all the other penguins in the colony. Parents have previously murmured their own characteristic call rhythm for weeks on end—as if the young birds require weeks to learn it perfectly. When once it has been acquired, the knowledge of individual vocal peculiarities seems to serve as an almost perfect means of recognition amongst a very dense crowd of birds of the same species, and tends to be particularly developed where nest territories are small, closely packed or ill-defined.

47

Although territorial proclamation and defence must be regarded as the main function of song, there are many species, such as the Bullfinch and Hawfinch, which possess complex songs but which do not utter them very loudly or persistently, and seldom or never from a conspicuous song-post. Such songs tend to be more variable and much less stereotyped than, for instance, are the songs of such a territorial group as the buntings. There seems little doubt that in birds in which the song is not primarily of territorial function, and sometimes in those in which it is, for example, Snow Bunting (Tinbergen, 1939), and Wren (Armstrong, 1955), it may serve a most important function in attracting a female to a male and subsequently influencing her behaviour in various ways. Song is thus part of the display and serves to reinforce and supplement the various other non-vocal components of sexual display. So it may play its part in initiating and controlling the development of the breeding-cycle, in preventing the mate from straying, once the pair-bond has been set up, and in synchronising a great many of the activities of the breeding-cycle—activities which are necessary for successful breeding and rearing of young but which can only so function if properly co-ordinated. Songs are sometimes specially differentiated for such purposes, as in the Grasshopper Sparrow (Smith, 1959).

Song is sometimes heard from migratory birds in the spring and tends to be stronger the nearer the bird is to its destination. The preliminary 'exploratory singing' of the Wren when exploring an unfamiliar territory may be similar in origin to that of the migrant with its journey still uncompleted (Armstrong, 1955). This species has a beautiful nest-invitation song, a part of the nest-invitation display. Similar nest-invitation displays including song are found in the Collared Flycatcher, the Redstart and a number of warblers. Armstrong (1955, p. 128) draws an interesting comparison between the courtship sequence of the male and female stickleback and the male and female Wren. The use of song for co-ordinating flock movements is not unknown. It has been reported in the Song Sparrow by Nice, and in the Wren, under the heading 'Rallying song', by Armstrong (1955).

Song from female birds is unusual or exceptional, particularly where there is striking sexual dimorphism. Careful studies with marked birds have revealed, however, that it is commoner than was formerly supposed in some species. Thus female Song Sparrows occasionally sing early in the season before nest-building begins and Nice (1943) lists about twenty species in which elaborate songs have been heard from both sexes. Where the female takes the initiative in courtship, as in the phalaropes, button quails, Painted Snipe, tinamous and coucals, this sex has the more elaborate vocalisations. Where there is marked division of labour in the process of nesting, territory-holding, and rearing young, song from both sexes would pro-bably be of no benefit and might simply cause confusion, if not worse. In some species, for example the Robin, both sexes hold territories at least temporarily in the autumn, and song from the female then seems to be more usual. Skutch (1954, p. 94) records that the female Orange-billed Sparrow sings while incubating. The female Wren has a quiet though arti-culate whisper-song, the function of which is obscure but seems to be in some way related to the care of the young (for example, brooding, feeding nestlings or fledged young, leading chicks from the nest or into the roost) and this song is also used occasionally by the males during territorial quarrels. However, full territorial song by female Wrens is very exceptional. A special form of hasty or 'congested' song has been described in this and a number of other species prior to or during copulation.

A peculiarly interesting case of female song is that which occurs in duetting, when two members of a pair sing simul-taneously as part of the courtship display or to maintain the pair-bond. This has been described for several species among the Furnariidae (spinetails, ovenbirds, etc.) and in the genera *Cinclus*, *Hylocichla* and *Richmondena*. In woodpeckers (*Centurus*, *Melanerpes*) both sexes communicate concerning the suitability of a nest-site by tapping, and mutual tapping performances may also help to strengthen the pair-bond (Kilham, 1959). In some trogons, barbets, South American Tyrannidae, Central American wrens and South African Laniidae, to mention only a few (van Tyne and Berger, 1959, cite fourteen or fifteen families) a very special type of duetting known as antiphonal singing occurs. In this type, two members of a pair may alternate with extraordinarily accurate timing, often singing different phrases so that unless one is actually watching it may be impossible to tell that the song is not coming from one bird.

It seems worth while describing one or two examples of this. I myself have heard it in the Marbled Guiana Quail, a bird of the Central American rain forest. The duet consists of a hurried breathless repetition of the words *corcorovado, corcorovado* with a rapid upward inflection on the *va*. One bird, presumably the male, contributes *corcoro* and the other *vado* with no perceptible break between. The performance has been excellently described by Armstrong (1947). The reciprocity is so perfect that one would never suspect that two birds were co-operating. Skutch (1940) describes the songs of some of the Central American wrens (birds of low tropical thickets) as being so perfectly harmonised and synchronised that, unless the listener chances to stand between the birds and hears the voice come now from this side and now from that, he may never suspect that he is not listening to the protracted song of a single bird. He cites the Tawny-bellied Wren, *Pheugopedius hyperythrus*, as especially note-worthy for its performances of this character. Another wren, *Thyrophilus modestus*, found throughout much of Central America, is called in Costa Rica *Chinchirigui*, a word which gives an excellent paraphrase of its loud, clear song. Skutch says that one member of the pair calls *chinchiri* while the mate answers *gui*. They repeat these sharp whistles over and over again with great rapidity and never a break in continuity, as though the sounds arose from a single throat. The closely related *Thyrophilus galbraithi* of Panama sings in the same antiphonal fashion.

The significance of these remarkable performances is by no means understood. Reading of the literature suggests that they are probably much more widespread than is at present realised, and this fact—if fact it be—again suggests that they are more characteristic of birds of dense vegetation and secretive habits so that only under particularly favourable circumstances is the true state of affairs likely to be perceived. The phenomenon is also in evidence in the elaborate courtship dances of the manakins (Pipridae), also birds of the Central and South American tropical rain forest. Snow (1956) has described how in the manakin *Chiroxiphia pareola* a perfectly co-ordinated duet takes place, performed by two males in front of one female. The explanation suggests itself that birds living in the dark and tangled undergrowth of tropical forests, conditions which are likely to hinder the development of mutual visual displays, are the more likely to replace these by the elaboration of vocal displays. It is perhaps also significant that in Europe the only group which seems to employ antiphonal vocalisation persistently is the owls which are, of course, mainly nocturnal.

It has long been known that the secretion of testicular hormone is one of the prime factors in bringing a song bird into the condition in which it is prepared to sing. The onset of territorial behaviour in the spring, behaviour which includes establishment of a territory, interest in nest-sites, aggressiveness towards males of the same species and vocalisation, all coincide with the seasonal growth in the testes and the corresponding increase in the secretion of the hormone (Bullough, 1942). It is also known that birds can be induced to sing out of season by the injection of testosterone propionate. Thus Thorpe (1958a) succeeded in producing song from male Chaffinches in mid-winter by such injections, although full song—that is, with the complete end-phrase—was never quite developed. Herrick and Harris (1957), adopting a relatively new hormone preparation, testosterone phenylacetate ('Perandren'/CIBA), obtained song in female canaries as a result of injection. First attempts to sing were similar to those of young males but after about seven days vigorous singing, indistinguishable from that of male birds and lasting for nearly a month, was obtained. I have also attempted to produce song in female Chaffinches by massive doses of testosterone propionate, but this was less successful than was the phenylacetate in canaries. With this preparation only one bird produced a sequence of notes having a slight resemblance to full song, but with the phenylacetate it has been possible to induce something resembling male Kaspar Hauser song in female Chaffinches (Thorpe, in press). Nice and ter Pelkwyk suggest that 'song was originally present in both sexes, and that there were two lines of evolution, one where the male had developed the more elaborate song, the other where the female did so' (Nice, 1943). Van Tyne and Berger (1959) point out that female birds are heterogametic and that the gonads of each sex secrete both male and female sex hormones. It is well known that in both sexes of mammals there is a delicate balance in the production of androgens and oestrogens and that the imbalance of these hormones results in changes in behaviour and secondary sex characters. It has been demonstrated experimentally in ducks that the ovary is responsible for the sexual dimorphism in the development of the osseus bulla and the genital tubercle, the female sex hormone inhibiting the development of the male-type syrinx and penis (see Lewis and Dobb, 1948). It is clear, then, that testosterone secretion has an enormous influence on the development of the song. Not only is the production of an innate song-pattern dependent upon the testicular secretion being at the right level, there is no doubt that the hormone level also governs, to some extent at any rate, the ability of the bird to learn songs. The autumn song-period which is shown by a number of birds in northern latitudes may also be accounted for in part by the autumnal recrudescence of the gonads which so often shows itself in an interest in nest-sites, territorial behaviour and other associated features. There is good evidence that the external stimuli which initiate and to some extent govern the seasonal hormone cycle, on which so much of the breeding-behaviour depends, include light (duration, quality and intensity), temperature, humidity and of course those more subtle features of the visual environment which are supplied by the sight of the territory with its seasonal changes in vegetation. But there is now no doubt that light changes are of overriding importance as a control factor. If finches, such as the Greenfinch or the Chaffinch, are subjected to a gradually decreasing day-length from artificial light in a light-controlled chamber from about the middle of June until after one month they are in almost complete darkness, they will, of course, cease to sing and it will be found that their gonads have regressed. In an experiment of this nature (Thorpe, 1958a) Chaffinches thus treated were kept in virtual darkness from 5 to 19 July, when they were given $1\frac{1}{2}$ h artificial daylight daily until 7 August. Then a gradually increasing daily illumination was supplied until by 5 September they were enjoying a 14-h illumination daily. On this date subsong was heard; it increased daily and became generally prevalent by 15 September, by which date the artificial day period was at its maximum duration of 16 h. This 16-h day was then maintained till most of the birds were in full song by the middle of November. It was found that the onset of song is more closely related to the length of time since the period of illumination started to increase than to the absolute length of the period. The experiment showed that maturation by artificial control of illumination can be as effective as is normal daylight in eliciting full song, although of course the intensity of the illumination supplied was far less than that of nature. This method of song-production by control of illumination is one that has long been known to bird-fanciers and is employed by Dutch bird-catchers when they wish to have singing-birds in cages for use as bait for passing migrants (Damsté, 1947; Hoos, 1937).

There are probably no birds whose song is absolutely constant in amount daily throughout the year. Cox (1944) gives a series of histograms showing the variation in the number of individuals of different species singing during daily morning and evening transects from February to October in the year 1942–3. His results are summarised in fig. 24 (see also Armstrong, 1955). Besides the annual song-cycle there is, of course, a daily song-cycle. Most species sing less during the middle of the day than they do in the early morning and later afternoon. The midday decrease in the amount of song is often associated with heat and wind and is especially noticeable in desert areas. In many species song is less evident in cloudy weather and on dull days, but rain itself may have little effect on singing. Indeed increased humidity often seems to stimulate bird-song, but the influence of this factor is very hard to disentangle from that of other factors which are also apt to vary concomitantly. In many birds of temperate regions there are periodical bursts of song which commence about dawn, or slightly before, and which are gradually reduced as the day proceeds, until near midday there is practically no song. Song-bouts are resumed in the afternoon at lesser intensity and without reaching the peak of activity of the morning song-period. In some species the morning or dawn song differs both in form and intensity from the evening song, and both are different in pattern from the day-time song. Skutch records that the Red Ant Tanager and the Blue Honeycreeper both have dawn songs which are rarely if ever uttered after sunrise (Skutch, 1954, p. 390).

Many activities other than song show a pronounced morning and evening peak, with the evening peak usually lower than that in the morning. The evidence for this has been well documented by Finnish workers (Klokaars, 1941; Palmgren, 1932,

53

1949). Curio in his recent study of the Pied Flycatcher (1959) shows that once the song of the male has attained its typical intensity early in the breeding-season, it is only the frequency of repetition which remains variable. In the morning the male sings about six phrases per minute, and less industriously in the afternoon. Curio finds that the correlation of song-intensity and air-temperature is approximately expressed by the formula $G = 2\cdot2 + 0\cdot33\,t$, where G = phrases per minute and t = tempera-

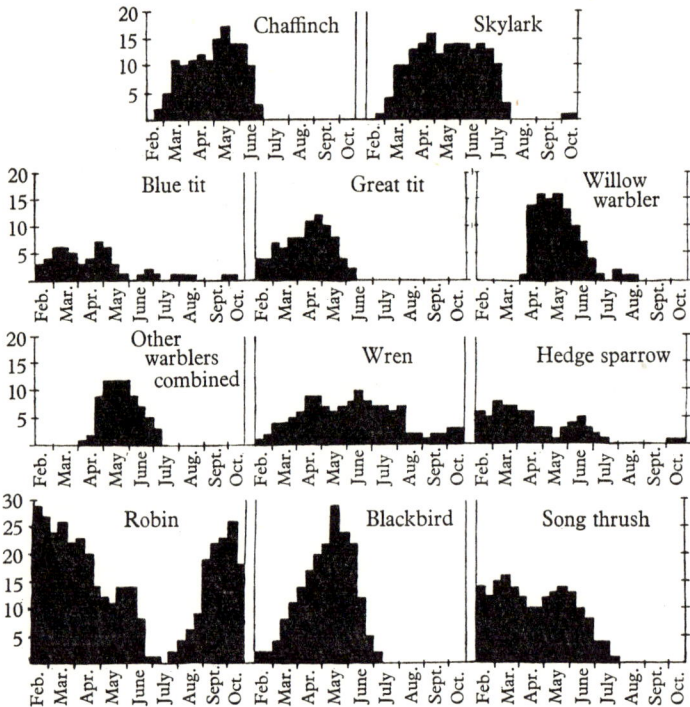

Fig. 24. Histograms showing the seasonal course of bird-song during one year. (Cox, 1944.)

ture in ° C. He finds that the song-intensity is typical for a given individual in a given stage of its reproductive cycle and fluctuates endogenously at short intervals. It is no doubt this endogenous fluctuation which gives rise to the periodical waves or bursts of song every few minutes or half-hour within the daily song-period. The internal factors which control these short-period rhythms are as yet not at all understood. There is no evidence that they can be primarily hormonal and one has to assume provisionally that they are neurogenic. This does not of course necessarily imply that they are innate; the neurogenic rhythm may have been imprinted by early experience, or otherwise learnt. However, since the frequency of bursts of song is in so many cases characteristic of the species, it seems reasonable to assume that there is, for some at any rate of these rhythms of singing, an innate neurogenic pacemaker. The Red-eyed Vireo is described as singing more or less continuously throughout the day and with little regard for weather or seasons (de Kiriline, 1954).

CHAPTER 4

The Characteristics of Full song and Subsong

As we have seen, the chief characteristics of full song (also called true song or primary song) are that it is of considerable duration in time, containing usually a variety of kinds of notes, and displaying a consistent overall pattern. Where the song is territorial in function it tends to be loud and frequent. In the pattern of the song, frequency, rhythm, timing, vocal quality, accent and grouping all play their part. In view of what has been said earlier about the main functions of song, we should expect to find in it characteristics or qualities which would render it effective for:

(1) acting as a specific recognition mark;
(2) making it readily localisable;
(3) giving it carrying power;
(4) providing individual, as distinct from specific, recognition marks.

Every field-naturalist knows, of course, that bird-songs are among the most useful features for specific identification, and there is not the slightest doubt that these features are appreciated by the bird's ear as well as by our own. In fact it is virtually impossible to think of two closely related species of birds which, possessing full song, are not thereby specifically distinguishable. Possible exceptions are discussed in chapter 6. Thus there is eloquent evidence for the importance of song as an isolating factor, and I think there can be no doubt that it is this requirement which has been the chief agent acting, in the course of evolution, to produce songs of increasing elaboration—such elaboration involving in some measure all the characteristics of song listed above. To take some examples, almost at random, from common European birds: in the buntings we might mention the Cirl, Corn, Yellow and Reed Bunting—all closely related members of the genus *Emberiza*, and all occurring in the same general geographical locality. The Goldcrest and Firecrest present another striking pair. Turning to the warblers, and restricting ourselves to those on the British list, we have Chiff-chaff, Willow Warbler and Wood Warbler, Garden Warbler, Sedge Warbler, Reed Warbler, Marsh Warbler, Great Reed Warbler, Moustached Warbler, Whitethroat and Lesser White-throat—all readily identifiable by song. It will be noted that in almost all these instances the striking differences concern duration, temporal pattern, pitch and accent, and much less tonal quality generally. On the other hand, it is often extra-ordinarily difficult to find generic or family characteristics in bird voices; and this of course is understandable since if closely related species are so different, it must follow that it will be hard to find generic similarities and consistencies. Where, on the other hand, we do find generic resemblances in songs, the common feature is more generally the quality of the voice and it seems a not unreasonable assumption that these are usually explicable as an expression of similarity in the structure of the vocal organs—although of course it may also indicate the existence of precise mechanisms in controlling modulation in frequency and in time. Moreover, we may also find generic or family characteristics in the duration of the song or song out-bursts. Marler, in discussing the relative uselessness of songs for defining higher systematic categories, particularly in those groups where they provide good specific differences, points out that if song is a factor in reproductive isolation, the songs are likely to be highly divergent between two closely allied sym-patric species. Therefore, in such cases there will have been intense selection for specific distinctiveness; but, conversely, similarity between the songs within a genus would confer no evolutionary advantages at all, and in fact is even likely to be dysgenic. One of the few large groups of song birds known to me which seems to show some general feature of song charac-teristic of the group is the buntings. Perhaps one could make out a similar case for the wrens and the thrushes. Thorpe and Lade (1961) have shown that the songs of the Emberizidae tend to be short, frequent and rather simple. An exception to this is the Lapland Bunting (fig. 25) which, in its treeless environment, sings on the wing and has a song which is longer and more complex, and which is also repetitive, like the Skylark's; these features presumably are an adaptation to aerial singing.

57

There are a number of other features more or less characteristic of bunting song, but the characterisation of the group by song is nevertheless far from easy, and tends to be negative rather than positive. Indeed, it is hard to avoid the conclusion that many of the features of bunting songs are an expression of general similarity of breeding organisation and the fact that the song is of prime use as a territorial proclamation, and that such common features as there are could well be due as much to convergence as to a common ancestry.

It is obvious that the more complex a bird's song becomes, the greater is the opportunity for individual variation to occur, and so it becomes possible for the species to be characterised by the main features of the song and yet for there to be a sufficient

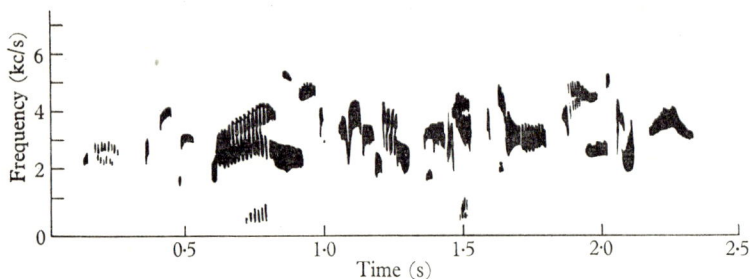

Fig. 25. Lapland Bunting song. In comparison with most species of Emberizidae, this song is long, complex and repetitive—characteristics which are probably an adaptation to aerial singing. (Thorpe and Lade, 1961.)

degree of variability to make it easy to recognise the individual solely by its voice. Indeed, it seems, from the study of the Chaffinch and many other examples, that one of the functions of complexity in song is to make possible songs which are both individually and specifically recognisable. The features of songs which most often confer specific distinctiveness are those of total duration, the occurrence of characteristic phrases, motifs or progressions and the acoustic quality of the notes. The way in which this individual characterisation is achieved will be discussed in a later chapter.

It is obvious that songs must have sufficient carrying power—in fact be loud enough in the appropriate frequencies—to perform their biological functions. It is seldom possible to give any exact estimate of the volume of song in decibels; but there is little doubt that, in general, birds with territorial songs sing louder and are audible over a greater range than are birds with non-territorial songs. Finally, in the matter of direction-giving, it is clear that if the song is to serve its purpose in advertising territory and attracting and retaining a mate, it is important that the bird should be readily localised by it—in other words, the song must have within it notes which give adequate clues for localisation. It can almost always be found that the songs of territorial species contain frequent repetitions of notes, themselves of short duration and considerable frequency distribution. The lower frequencies are likely to be of a wavelength which allows the two ears of the hearer to detect phase difference. These notes also give clues to direction in the form of intensity and time of arrival of the sound at the two ears, the latter because the sound comes as a click-like pulse. So we can sum up by saying that the typical song of a territory-defending song bird has features which can very plausibly be attributed to the need to provide a specific yet individually recognisable utterance and one which gives plenty of clues for direction.

A glance at the sound spectrograms of bird vocalisations shows that extreme high front sounds are common (fig. 26). These are sounds containing a big range of frequencies and of very short duration, that is 1–20 ms; they are often heard as clicks by our ears, lacking any definite pitch (see fig. 27). There seems little doubt that the exact manner of onset of such sounds, represented by the initial slope of the mark on the sound spectrogram, may have a big influence in conferring distinctive tonal quality —at any rate as perceived by our ears—on sounds which are in themselves (as is clear from the sound spectrogram) largely devoid of any harmonic partials which we normally think of as essential for the production of a recognisable tone. These very rapid changes in characteristic sounds in a brief note immediately after onset are what is normally referred to as 'transients'. It is not necessary to assume that the bird vocal-organs are themselves actively modifying the sound during this very brief of its change. On the contrary, the transients are the result of the method of starting the sound, and once the sound has been started they are determined by the general structure of the vocal-organs rather than by any methods of vocal control that the bird may have at its disposal. How far these different transients may confer a detectable vocal quality on the notes which display them is chiefly a question of the speed of response of the hearing organs of the recipient. It is difficult to obtain exact information on this latter point except by long-continued and most laborious training experiments. However, while these

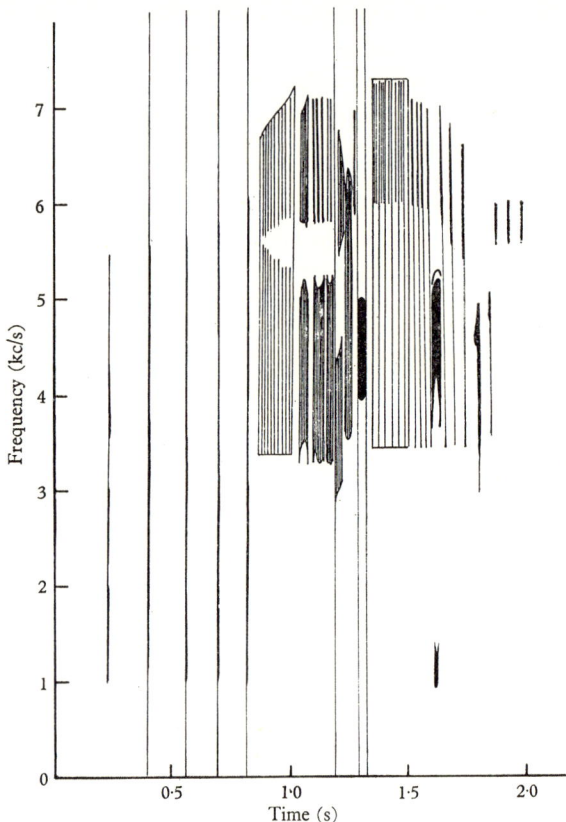

Fig. 26. Corn Bunting song, showing sounds with big range of frequencies and very short duration, often heard as clicks. (Thorpe and Lade, 1961.)

have never been systematically carried out, our observations on the song of the Chaffinch show that there may be as many as forty-five separate notes per second, with an interval of 0·01 s between them, and in training experiments I have myself produced a good imitation which involved the recognition and copying by the bird of notes of $\frac{1}{10}$ s duration, separated by an interval of about 10 ms (Thorpe, 1958 a). Ansley (1954) has also produced some evidence that the bird hearing-organs have a higher 'flicker fusion frequency' (to borrow a term from the students of visual physiology) than has man.

Acoustically pure tones are almost if not quite absent from bird vocalisations. However, as everyone knows, there are sounds of sufficient purity and translucency to strike us as flute-like or bell-like (see figs. 4, 5, 29, 50 etc.), and some of them have regular harmonics (see fig. 28). The evidence goes to show, however, that

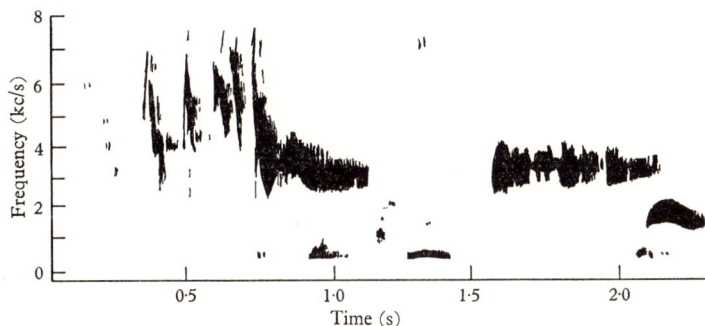

Fig. 27. Robin song, showing high front sounds and extensive slurring. (Thorpe, 1959.)

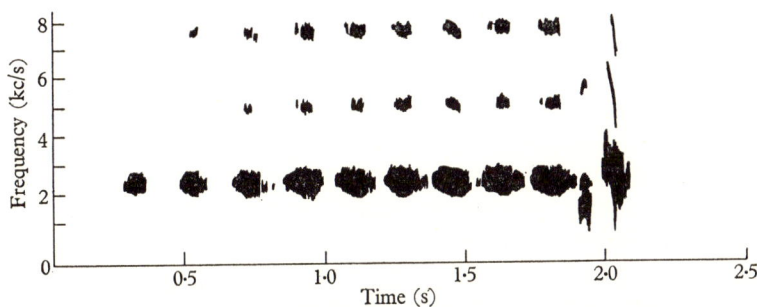

Fig. 28. Note from Nightingale song, showing regular harmonics.

the pitch-constancy of a bird such as the Blackbird, while remarkable enough, does not compare with that of a fully trained human musician possessing the sense of absolute pitch. There tends to be a considerable amount of vibrato around the main frequency (see fig. 29). It is true, however, that birds can sing in the same pitch day after day with only a minimum of variation, and it is also true that they can transpose within limits. Thus one of my experimental Chaffinches practised a song-ending at one

61

pitch *sotto voce*, but when producing it at full strength, sang it in another pitch, and Gooch (1952) has recorded changes of pitch in a Cirl Bunting. The human ear is extraordinarily accurate as a frequency or pitch discriminator, the error being only about 4 cycles over a considerable part of the range. But the 'time-perception smear' of the human-being is large—approximately 5 cs. There is some evidence that the bird's pitch-discrimination is as good as that of human-beings; time-perception characteristics are probably better—perhaps by a factor of 10.

It is known that human-beings can achieve surprisingly good localisation of a complex sound even when only one ear is in operation (Stevens and Davis, 1938). This is done by forming a subjective standard of intensity in a few trials and after this

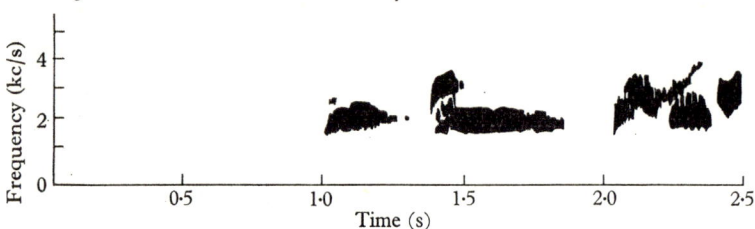

Fig. 29. Blackbird. 'Pure' note from song, showing vibrato around main frequency. (Hall-Craggs, 1961.)

experience the tones heard behind are the weaker ones, and those heard in front are the strong ones. It is thought, with good reason, that sound-shadows from the external ear must account for this effect. It thus becomes no longer surprising that complex tones and noises can, under certain circumstances, be localised with relative ease even in the absence of the machinery for binaural comparison. When both low and high frequencies are present, the low frequencies provide cues in the form of phase-differences and the high frequencies by intensity-differences; and the two types of cue reinforce one another. Moreover, the attenuation of high-frequency components of sounds coming from behind the listener alters both quality and intensity (Stevens and Davis, 1938). The result is that such complex sounds can be located with greater accuracy than pure tones. In fact the accuracy with which *experienced* human beings can locate a complex sound-pattern is not greatly lessened by being made monaurally instead of binaurally (Angell and Fite, 1901).

Fig. 30 shows sound spectrograms of representative bird-notes of strikingly different tonal qualities. These figures make clear the influence of the acoustic structure of the sound as portrayed by the sound spectrograph in determining the tonal quality of the sound for our own ears, and presumably also for the bird's.

In spite of all that has been said above in respect of the advantage for song birds of developing a high degree of complexity in their vocal utterances, we do find a great deal of

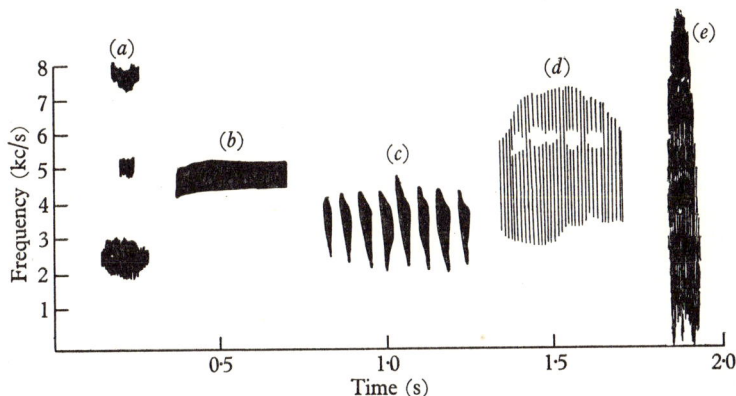

Fig. 30. A representative series of bird notes showing strikingly different tonal quality. (a) Nightingale note, very pure, with harmonics; (b) White-throated Sparrow, clear whistle; (c) Marsh Warbler, musical trill; (d) Clay-coloured Sparrow, toneless buzz; (e) Budgerigar, noisy flight squawk.

elaboration which goes beyond anything which would seem to be biologically advantageous. The vocal gymnastic ability to be discussed in the final chapter is only one of these features. The Nightingale's song is another instance in which the elaboration of pattern seems to have gone to quite excessive lengths, unless indeed we suppose that the listening bird has something approaching aesthetic appreciation and is more stimulated by a nightingale song of high elaboration than by one that is simpler. Koehler (1951) regards bird-song as a kind of performance which could be the first step both towards music and speech. This matter has also been considered by Lorenz— (see Craig, 1943; Thorpe, 1956) in connection with the evolution of tonal purity in bird-voices. Lorenz had made the point that the purity of colour of some visual social releasers—as in the duck's speculum—could be of selective value, since they have to be seen against the complex inanimate or non-animal background containing every shade of colour. Song, he argues, encounters virtually no non-biological competition since there are practically no sounds of inanimate origin which are of such frequency or such form as to compete. Here, however, there seems to be a possible flaw in the argument, for surely once a bird vocalisation has acquired a specific signal function, vigorous interspecific competition for the available frequency-range will be initiated. Thus purity of tone will at once become a potentially advantageous feature, since, in common with the tendency to elaborate the pattern of the sounds, it will provide an additional dimension for distinctiveness and therefore should lead—like the international agreement on the allocation of radio frequencies—to an economic and peaceful utilisation of the available spectrum. But even admitting this, it is hard to imagine any selective reason for the extreme purity of some bird-notes, since the releaser function does appear to have been transcended in many cases. It may be that tonal purity, the inventiveness shown in the individual characteristics of bird-songs and the imitative ability of many birds (which will be discussed in a subsequent chapter) are all further examples of what, for want of a better term and to cloak our present ignorance, may be described as pre-adaptation; that is pre-adaptation for apparently remote and unlikely contingencies. It is as if specialisation has gone in advance of immediate adaptive requirements.

Subsong

Aviculturalists and bird-fanciers have for long used the term 'recording' to denote the very quiet practice-like singing so often heard from captive birds before they come into the phase of true song (Thorpe and Pilcher, 1958). It has often been asserted that the instrument known as the recorder originally took its name from the bird flageolet—which was used by bird-fanciers for teaching tunes to canaries, Bullfinches and other song birds; but it seems more likely that the song was named from the instrument and not vice versa. Many early naturalists noted from time to time the utterance by birds in the wild of sounds similar to this recording of tame birds. A number of examples are given by Thorpe and Pilcher (1958). Nicholson

(1927) was the first to employ the term 'subsong', which term was later developed by Nicholson and Koch (1936) simply to mean quiet song—that is, song of low volume. It was taken 'to include all performances which are so inwardly or faintly uttered that they do not carry to anywhere near the distance over which the bird is physically capable of making itself heard'. Lister (1953a) has abandoned this original broad use of the term subsong, replacing it by the term 'secondary song'. Secondary song is thus contrasted with the full song which he designates 'primary song'. Within his category secondary song Lister recognises 'whisper song', in which the *pattern* of the utterance is closely similar to that of primary song, and some other subcategories in which it is different. The chief of these subcategories is 'subsong' in his new more restricted sense. Nicholson himself pointed out that subsongs often lack territorial influence and provoke no visible hostility in other males, and this has been entirely borne out by my own experience and those of my associates, in that we have never been able to establish any specific communicatory function for these utterances in the Chaffinch.

Subsong has been most fully studied in the Chaffinch (Thorpe, 1955, 1958b; Thorpe and Pilcher, 1958). In this species the subsong, besides being of low intensity and dissimilar in pattern, also differs from the full song in a number of other respects. Whereas the full song consists of a well-defined burst of sound lasting between 2 and 3 s, subsong consists of an irregular and indefinite series of notes continuing perhaps for half a minute or more, although broken up into ill-defined phrases, each phrase lasting for perhaps 2 or 3 s. The notes in the Chaffinch subsong are very variable but nevertheless fall into two fairly well-defined groups—first, a variety of chirping and cheeping notes, and secondly, a series of mechanical-sounding rattles of varying pitch. The simplest type, which is usually heard from young males in their first autumn, consists of a series of chirping notes fluctuating in pitch. During this autumn period the beak is often closed while singing and the rattle is heard only infrequently. At this time of the year females occasionally give a similar subsong. In the late winter or early in spring the subsong is resumed, and after a week or so the bird may be spending a considerable part of its day in producing these utterances. The sound spectrograms, fig. 31, show that most of the notes themselves are different in structure from those which go to make up the full song and are particularly characterised by containing a much bigger range of frequencies—they are, in other words, very indefinite in pitch. In the Chaffinch, subsong seems to be most frequently and consistently produced by first-year males in the early spring, although it is also produced by older birds and is undoubtedly under the control of the seasonal increase of production of sex hormones. The view so often expressed by bird-fanciers that 'recording' is in the nature of practice is plausible up to a point in that subsong does seem to provide, in some degree, the raw material out of which, by practice and by the elimination of

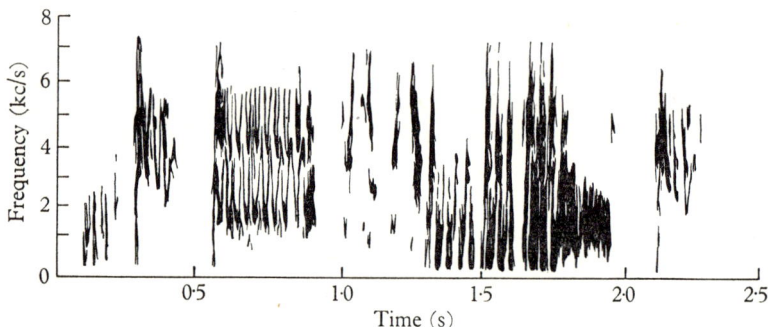

Fig. 31. Chaffinch. Subsong, showing chirps and rattles having big range of frequencies. (Thorpe, 1958a.)

unwanted extremes of frequency, the full song is so to speak crystallised. This crystallising process is seen in fig. 32. It consists essentially of the building up of comparatively complex song on the basis provided by the innate or inborn song. This to some extent involves picking up notes and phrases from other Chaffinches with which the bird may be singing in competition in its territory, and in part it entails the incorporation of sounds characteristic of the subsong. Although the subsong of the Chaffinch in the wild sometimes seems to be associated with territory and may be given from song-posts and while feeding or preening on the ground, it does not appear to convey territorial information and is more usually given from dense cover. This is undoubtedly the reason why it is so often overlooked by the field observer. Moreover, the quality of the notes is such that the naturalist who knows only the full song would probably not recognise the utterance as coming from a Chaffinch

66

at all. A study of records of the transition of the subsong into full song shows that at least some part of the process consists in discarding those more extreme frequencies which are not required in the full song. The belief that the subsong of the Chaffinch is non-communicatory is supported by another fact. Wild Chaffinches are non-imitative birds in the sense that they will not normally include in their full song sounds other than those which they have heard in the full songs of other Chaffinches. Yet when they sing the subsong they are much less particular, and it has been possible to recognise notes and phrases copied from canaries, tits (*Parus* spp.) and other birds in the subsongs of our experimental Chaffinches.

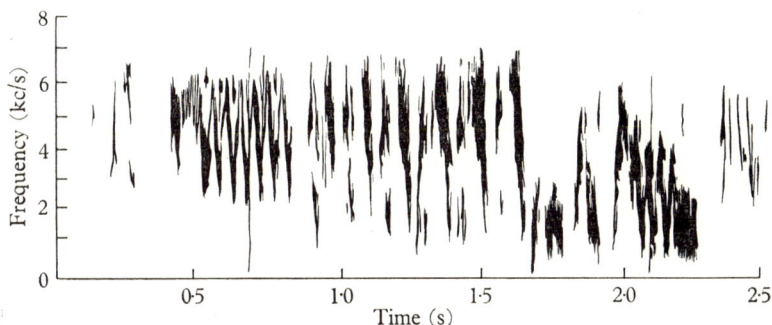

Fig. 32. Chaffinch. Subsong in transition to full song. (Thorpe, 1958*a*.)

If we base general conclusions as to the subsong on work on the Chaffinch, and this is after all the species which has been most thoroughly investigated, we conclude that subsong differs from full song in the following respects:

(1) The main fundamental frequency or 'pitch' is apt to be lower than in the full song;

(2) the frequency range of the subsong as a whole and of the individual notes of which it is composed tends to be greater;

(3) it is much quieter;

(4) the overall pattern of notes comprising the utterance is entirely different;

(5) the lengths of phrases of the song-bursts are different, tending to be longer;

(6) subsong is characteristic of lower sexual motivation, being generally produced earlier in the breeding-season;

(7) there is some evidence that, especially in young birds, the subsong is in the nature of practice for the full song.

Having established these points of difference with regard to the Chaffinch, it obviously becomes interesting to inquire whether similar differences hold good with other species. There are as yet still far too few complete recordings of the song repertoire of enough species to enable any dogmatic conclusions to be arrived at as to the general applicability

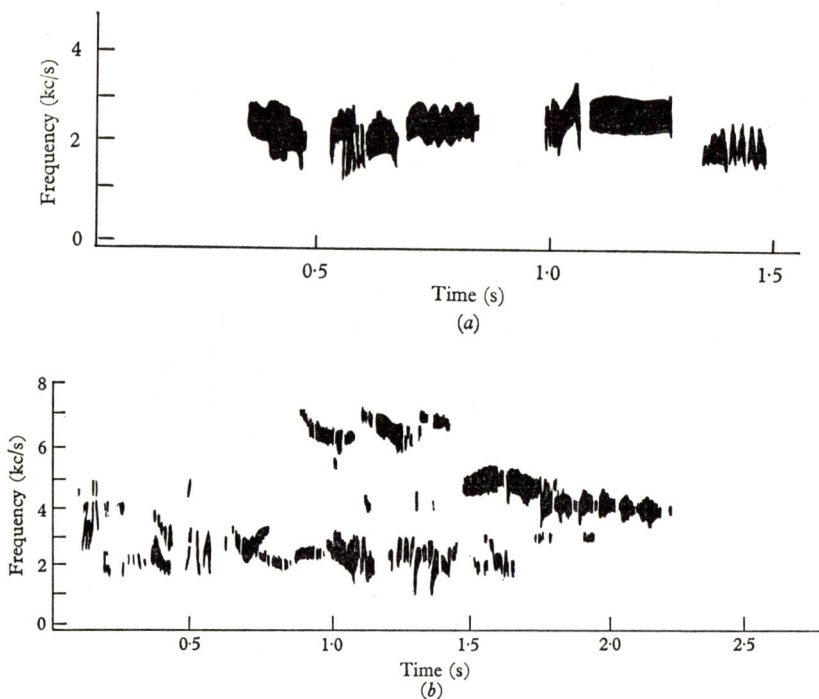

Fig. 33. Mistle Thrush. (a) Typical phrases from full song; (b) corresponding phrases from subsong. Note harsh impure notes, big frequency-range and rambling ill-defined phrases. (Thorpe and Pilcher, 1958.)

of the criteria outlined above. It stands to reason that subsong as at present defined is most likely to be recognised in species in which the full song is a loud and fairly stereotyped utterance in use as a territorial proclamation. In other species where the song seems to have little territorial function, and indeed seems to serve primarily, if not exclusively, as a component of sexual display and for maintaining and co-ordinating the behaviour of the mated pair throughout the breeding-season, subsong may prove to be less readily separable as a distinct category.

The Turdidae and Icteridae probably supply the best material, apart from the Chaffinch, for study of subsong. The Western Meadow Lark, Blackbird, and Song Thrush, provide examples of what appears to be subsong, answering

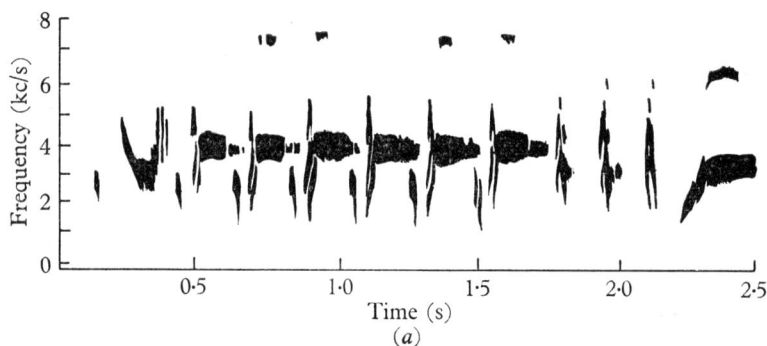

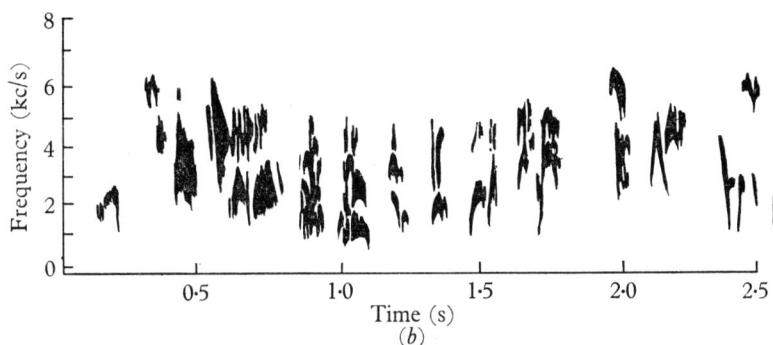

Fig. 34. Canary. (a) Typical phrases from full song. Note purity of notes. (b) corresponding phrases from juvenile song. Note impurity of notes, containing much lower frequencies than those in (a). (Thorpe and Pilcher, 1958.)

in most, if not all, respects to the definitions given above. Moreover, in both species there is evidence suggesting that the subsong is in the nature of practice. The Mistle Thrush also provides good examples of subsong, except that in this instance we have as yet no clear evidence that the average main frequency of the fundamental is any lower. The same applies to the Redwing. Apart from the Meadow Lark, the thrushes and the Chaffinch, there is no other species in which at present there is any good reason to suppose that the subsong serves as practice; although of course it must be remembered that the estimation of the evidence of this is at best a subjective matter.

Both the canary and the American Goldfinch have subsongs which are typical enough in all respects save that there is no marked difference in the duration of the song bursts as between the two types of utterance. Coming to the buntings, the position is more obscure and one hesitates to say whether in fact subsong is present or not. Records of the Yellow Bunting suggest that the early incomplete song contains lower frequencies than does the full song, and similarly has a greater frequency range. The Corn Bunting also shows a subsong of lower pitch and volume, which in addition displays some slight differences in pattern. Finally, the Hedge Sparrow apparently has a subsong in which differences of frequency-range, volume and pattern all seem to be clear. I think, however, we may safely guess that as further material comes to hand, subsong will be found to be a very widespread phenomenon amongst song birds. Lister (1953 b) has recorded many cases of secondary song in Indian birds and he has generously supplied me with detailed notes on subsong of many species of English birds mentioned above, and in addition the Wren, Great Tit, Pied Wagtail and Garden Warbler. Here is a line of investigation which offers much scope both for the aviculturalist and the field-naturalist equipped with a good tape-recorder. Such people have an excellent opportunity to collect material which may prove of great value in furthering the understanding of vocal communication in birds. Figs. 33 and 34 give some further examples of some of the characteristics of subsong outlined in this chapter.

CHAPTER 5

The Development of Song in the Individual

IN the previous chapter we considered the various characteristics, acoustic and otherwise, of subsong and discussed the value and significance of the term as applied to bird-song in general. In the present chapter it is proposed to consider the process of development of song out of subsong.

At its simplest, the early subsong of the Chaffinch comprises a steady series of chirping notes, suggesting such words as *tchirp*, *tcheep*, *tchip*, *seep*, etc., fluctuating in pitch, with little or

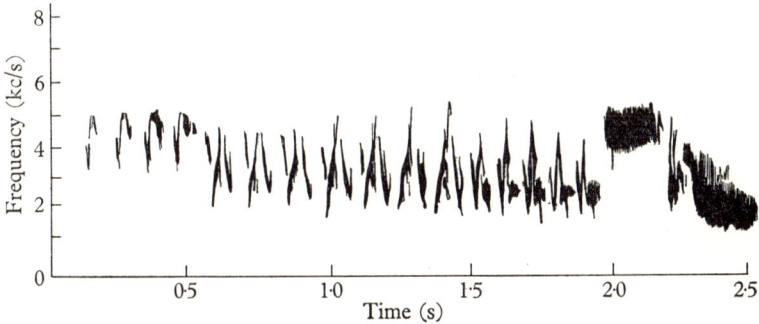

Fig. 35. Chaffinch. Song of a young bird, 4 May 1957. The song is still too loose and long as compared with the normal full song of the species. (Thorpe, 1958a.) Compare with Figs. 18 and 36.

no evidence of the rattle. As the spring comes on, subsong becomes more frequent and the rattle more and more evident amongst the *tchirp* sequences. If undisturbed, the young male will start a more intense phase of his subsong soon after he enters his new territory in the spring. Later the subsong shows further progressive changes. Sound spectrograms of records made at this time indicate the pattern of the full song as it were crystallising out from the more amorphous subsong (see fig. 32 above). By the latter part of March or early in April, in a normal season, a young bird of the year will have produced a song which is now quite recognisably that of a Chaffinch, although it may still have characteristic phrases of the subsong such as the rattle interspersed here and there in it, or tacked on at the end or the beginning; so the song is still much too loose and too long as compared with the normal full song of the species. Fig. 35 shows the song of a young bird on 4 May 1957. This could be regarded as normal, although there is not yet quite the clear division into three phrases which is usual in the Chaffinch song, and the number of notes is above average. However, during this part of the season a rapid process of tightening and integration takes place, and fig. 36 shows the stage which this particular bird had reached four days later,

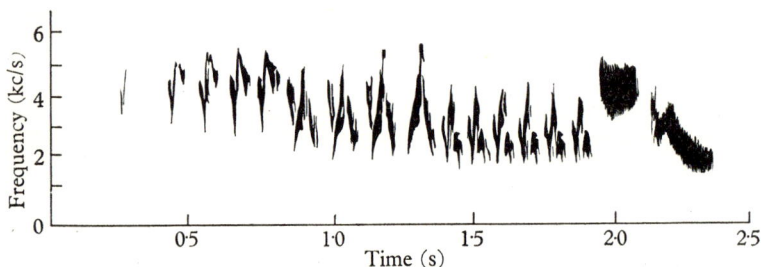

Fig. 36. Chaffinch. Same bird as fig. 35, 4 days later, showing rapid process of tightening and integration. (Thorpe, 1958a.)

on 8 May 1957. It can now be regarded as a normal example of Chaffinch full song. What then has really happened in this process of 'crystallisation'? What is it that crystallises out of what?

The normal Chaffinch song has been described and illustrated in the last chapter. If, however, we take young Chaffinches from the nest at about five days of age and rear them by hand in auditory isolation from other members of their species until they produce their own independent songs in the following spring, we find that while the subsong of these isolated birds is not in any obvious respect abnormal, the song that they produce from this subsong is of an extremely simple and restricted type. An example is shown in fig. 37. It will be seen that almost all of what we regard as normal features of Chaffinch song are missing. In these songs there is only a very slight trace of division into phrases, and in most cases there is no terminal flourish, although the last note may be raised in mean frequency from about 1·5 to 3 kc. The mean frequency of notes in fact tends to be too low and the 'frequency envelope' of the song from start to finish is abnormal, usually being almost level or showing a slight and gradual descent. In fact the only respect in which these songs can be regarded as normal is that they are of about the right length and about the right number of notes, and that these notes are of fairly normal tonality in themselves, though of an abnormally uniform tonal quality—the first and last notes often being almost identical in structure. It seems, then, that these isolated Chaffinches have crystallised out from their subsong what can be regarded as the unlearned 'blueprint' of the Chaffinch song, a song-patttern which must in some

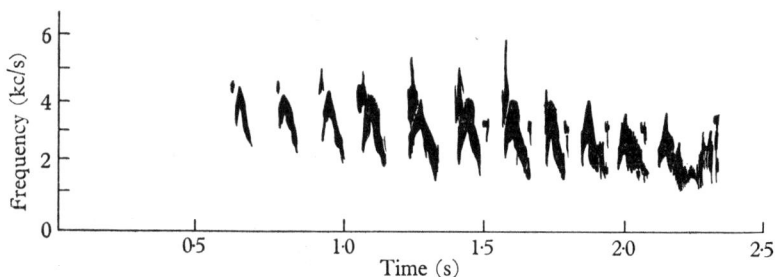

Fig. 37. Song of Kaspar Hauser Chaffinch. Hand-reared in auditory isolation. (Thorpe, 1958a.)

way be coded genetically in the germ plasm and transmitted thus into the central nervous organisation of the bird, and which can be produced without the assistance of any acoustic model to help in co-ordinating the parts or differentiating them. This much of the song-pattern is, in other words, self-differentiating.[1]

If now we hand-rear other individuals but, instead of keeping them isolated from all other birds until they commence singing themselves, we isolate them only from older and experienced Chaffinches, allowing them to hear other birds treated as they themselves have been, we get a very different result. What we have thus done is to make small communities of hand-reared birds, consisting of perhaps two, three, four or five birds per group, the individuals of which can hear each other but are, as a group, still totally isolated from all experience of normal Chaffinch song. In this kind of experiment each community of

[1] In the Blackbird, birds operatively deafened at the age of eighteen days, so that acoustic feed-back from the cochlea is eliminated, still perform many phrases of the song normally (Messmer & Messmer, 1956).

73

birds develops an entirely distinctive community pattern to which all the members of the group conform, often with extreme precision; the resemblance as between the songs of members of the same group is so close throughout that it is often difficult to distinguish them one from another, even when subjected to detailed analysis by sound spectrograph. Fig. 38 shows the song which was developed by two birds kept together in isolation during 1951 and 1952, having had no contact with any other birds at all. Fig. 19 (p. 42) also represents the song of a couple of birds kept together but otherwise completely isolated during 1952 and 1953. Fig. 20 is typical of the five songs developed by five members of another group, also kept together in isolation during the same year. It will be seen that some of

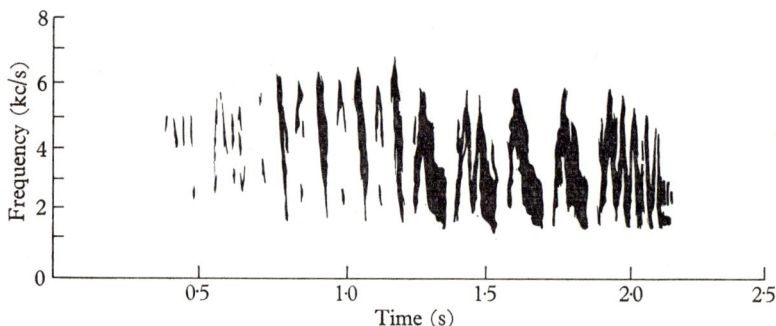

Fig. 38. Chaffinch. Song produced by one member of a Kaspar Hauser group of two unrelated birds. (Thorpe, 1958a.)

these songs are almost but not quite as simple as the isolate songs described above, others have developed a little way towards normality of song but completely lack anything that could be called a normal ending, while yet others have produced considerable complexity—but a complexity quite unlike anything that has yet been recorded in the wild.

If now, instead of taking young Chaffinches from the nest, we catch them in the autumn of their first year so that, as juveniles, they will already have heard some song in the wild, and if we keep these birds singly and again isolated so that they cannot hear any other Chaffinches, we find that they produce songs which are very much nearer normality than the birds treated in the manner just described. When they come to develop the song from the subsong in their first spring, they make them

74

out of the inborn component plus material heard in the previous autumn. This is shown in fig. 39. It is clear from the
study of such songs that the birds have, during the autumn,
learnt that the song 'should be' divided into three sections and
that a terminal flourish is appropriate as an ending. The next
step is to repeat this experiment but to keep the autumn-caught
birds together in small isolated communities so that again a
member of any one community will hear nothing but the songs
of its community-mates. Thus we now give the birds opportunity
to develop in the spring, songs constructed from (1) the inborn
component, (2) material heard the previous autumn, and
(3) material as elaborated by their cage-mates of similar

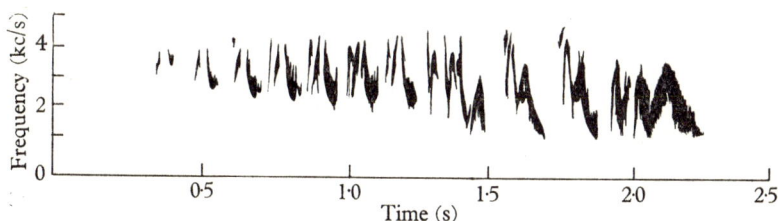

Fig. 39. Chaffinch. Song produced by a bird caught in the autumn of its first
year and prevented from hearing full song of other Chaffinches. The song is thus constructed out of the inborn component plus material heard in the previous autumn.
(Thorpe, 1958a.)

experience. Figs. 40 and 41 show what happens in this case.
Fig. 39 above shows what an autumn-caught first-year bird
was able to produce by itself, fig. 40 shows what such a bird
was able to produce after it had had the experience of
singing together with another bird of similarly restricted op-
portunities for a matter of about two weeks, that is, from
26 March to 8 April 1954. Similarly, fig. 41 shows what
the bird O/H was able to produce from its previous song
as a result of singing in June 1954 in company with one other
bird of similar experience. Thus these birds, by practising
together with other birds, were able to use the combination of
their inborn blueprint and previous autumn's experience to
better advantage—that is, they were able to achieve a more
normal song from their subsong by means of group practice.
Under these circumstances, it is found that there is a special

75

tendency for the birds of the same group to match their song-endings. The bird, O/H, whose song is shown in fig. 41 has matched the song-ending of its cage-mate.

From the experiments just described it appears, then, that the difference between the hand-reared birds and those which had

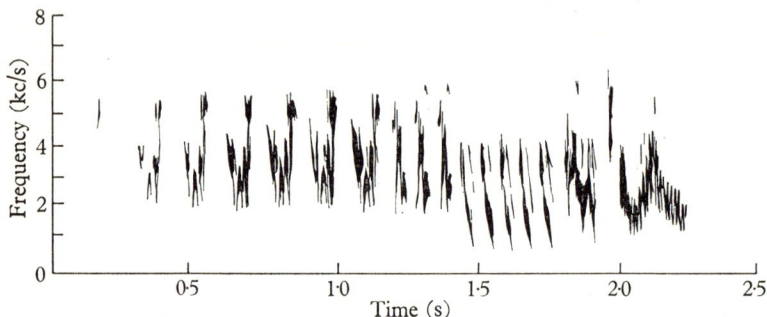

Fig. 40. Song of autumn-caught Chaffinch given opportunity the following spring to construct songs from (i) the inborn component, (ii) material heard the first autumn, (iii) material as elaborated by cage mates of similar experience. (Thorpe, 1958 a.)

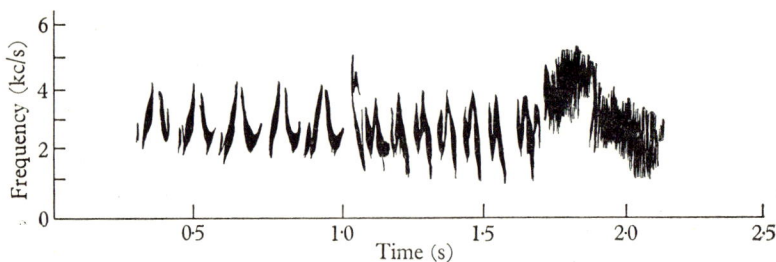

Fig. 41. Chaffinch. Song in first spring of bird caught in first autumn after having had opportunity to model its song on that of another bird of similar experience. (Thorpe, 1958 a.)

a normal fledgling and early juvenile life, but which were isolated from September onwards, is explicable only on the assumption that some peculiarities of the normal song have been learned or differentiated in the earliest youth, before the bird itself is able to produce any kind of full song. It seems that these birds have, by their first September, acquired the tendency to produce a three-phrase song—although the regularity with

76

which the songs of isolated birds also show a similar trend suggests that this characteristic must be latent in the blueprint of the innate pattern but incapable of expression without some help from associates. The birds which have had normal fledgling and early juvenile life appear also to have learned that the terminal phrase should contain a more or less elaborate flourish—a performance which the true isolates seem quite unable to emulate. The details of this terminal phrase with its flourish are apparently not learned in September but are worked out by members of the group in competitive singing the following spring. In the wild it seems that young Chaffinches must certainly learn some details of song from their parents or from other adults in the first few weeks of life. At this stage the young bird appears to absorb the general pattern of division of the song into two or three phrases, with a flourish at the end; but not until the critical period during the following spring does the bird develop the finer details of its song. This of course is the time when the young wild Chaffinch first sings in a territory in competition with neighbouring birds of the same species, and there is good evidence—as will be seen later—that it learns the details of song from these neighbours. It may in fact learn two or three different songs, sometimes even more, from neighbours on different sides of its territory. So we see that the full Chaffinch song is an integration of an inborn (or self-differentiating) and of a learned (or socially differentiated) song-pattern; the former constituting the basis for the latter. The isolated Chaffinches, as we have seen, can work out for themselves very strange songs. On the other hand, those in the wild are presumably circumscribed by the general pattern of the Chaffinch song characteristic of the locality, though of course they too may develop individual variations in detail.

  Although the experiments here described (see Thorpe, 1958a and b) have clearly established that the ability to perform the basic outline of the song is inborn and that the finer details are acquired by learning from associates, it is by no means easy to define precisely the limits of the inborn pattern of song. As we have seen, the completely isolated hand-reared bird can perform only the simplest songs (fig. 37). Yet even the stimulus provided by a singing competitor as inexperienced as itself will help it some way further towards normality—at least in so far as helping it to achieve the triple form and stepwise descent of

77

frequency. Also we have seen that once a bird has heard a 'flourish', in whatever circumstances, it seems to 'sense' that this is a sound appropriate for ending its song, and tends to use it accordingly. It seems then that while the innate tendency to produce the true Kaspar Hauser song is strong enough to govern the bird's behaviour even in complete isolation, there are other parts of the inborn pattern which, although genetically coded in the same way, need the trigger-like stimulus of competitive singing to enable them to emerge into the actuality of performance. Such relatively weak inherited tendencies, albeit strong enough ultimately to find their way out through experience, seem the necessary explanation of the fact that even long-isolated populations of Chaffinches, such as those of South Africa and New Zealand, while showing the same tendency to form local dialects, have nevertheless failed, even in the 60–80 or more years of their separation, to drift far away from the specific norm of Europe. Their songs are instantly recognisable as those of 'normal' Chaffinches no more divergent than some of the populations of Western Europe.

It will be clear to the student of animal learning and to those interested in learning theory generally, that this process of song-learning in the Chaffinch raises some interesting and puzzling problems. It is obviously a mimetic process in the simple sense that one bird can be said to be copying the actions of another. And this copying cannot readily be explained on any simple theory of conditioning since there is no obvious reward, in the sense of physiological reinforcement, secured by the bird as a result of its learning process. On the other hand, we must be careful about labelling it 'imitation' because the word usually implies a process at a rather high mental level which results in the copying of a novel or otherwise improbable act or utterance, or some act for which there is clearly no instinctive tendency. Thus visual imitation becomes something which apparently involves self-consciousness, something of intent to profit by another's experience, and it is in fact very doubtful whether (except possibly in cats) we find any certain examples of such behaviour anywhere in the animal kingdom below the primates. However, there is one respect in which vocal imitation differs rather significantly from the kind of imitation that can be found in primates. This is because, as McDougall pointed out long ago, the action of uttering a sound is unique amongst all actions in the important respect that whereas bodily action of any kind cannot be perceived by the actor in the same way in which it is perceived by his fellow creatures, and in which he perceives their bodily movements, the sounds he and they utter are presumably perceived by him and by them in much the same way. If we suppose that the animal is endowed by nature with a number of vocal motor mechanisms which enable it to utter a variety of sounds, then whenever one of these is set in action the animal hears its own voice uttering a corresponding sound. In consequence, the sense impression becomes associated with that motor mechanism. Now suppose the animal hears the same sounds uttered by another. The sound will have the same effect, namely it will already have been associated with the vocal motor mechanism. Thus we only have to suppose that there is some predilection for hearing a certain type of sound-pattern or a predilection for achieving vocal control of the sounds which it is capable of uttering, to realise that apparently very complex and elaborate imitation of sounds by birds might be explicable essentially on the basis of trial-and-error learning— the bird, so to speak, is 'playing about with' its vocal-organs until it produces a sound which is similar to or identical with the sound to which it has been listening. The essence of the point may be summed up by saying that while it is very difficult for a human being (and perhaps impossible for an animal) to see himself as others see him, it is much less difficult for him to hear himself as others hear him.

But assuming all this, another problem remains and that is why should the bird prefer to hear its own vocal apparatus making a sound which it has heard from another individual rather than hear it make a sound which is either entirely new or at any rate not related to the sounds made by other members of the species? Moreover, in the case of the Chaffinch, two further problems arise: First, why does the Chaffinch imitate the sounds of other Chaffinches but not the sounds produced by other species; and secondly, why is it that while the Chaffinch can learn during its first singing-season as many as six different songs from the different neighbours in adjacent territories, it does not add to its repertoire in later seasons? The evidence on this latter point seems quite clear: whatever song or songs an individual Chaffinch has learnt by the time it is about thirteen months old, they remain its song or songs for

79

the rest of its life. The learning-period is cut short abruptly in June or July of its first adult year and under no circumstances normally encountered does it apparently ever learn anything more. This restriction of learning to a period in the early life, a period which is brought to an abrupt close by internal factors not yet understood, but presumably hormonal in nature, recalls a similar restriction of learning-ability to a particular type of object and to a sharply defined sensitive period which has been called 'imprinting'[1]; and it is undoubtedly true that in some respects the song-learning of a bird such as the Chaffinch has important similarities with the process of imprinting. The onset of the period of maximum sensitivity for song-learning can be delayed by experimental techniques such as crowding and light-control, and can be correspondingly extended into the late summer, but once over it cannot—so far as we know—be renewed. In these respects too it resembles imprinting of young chickens during the following response.

An attempt was made to throw light on the first of these questions by trying to teach a Chaffinch artificial songs. It has for two centuries at least been common knowledge among bird-fanciers that some birds, for example, the Bullfinch, can be taught quite fancy songs by having these songs played to it on a pipe specially designed for the purpose and called the bird flageolet—or indeed simply by whistling with the lips. The modern development of tape-recorders suggested another way of doing this, and so a tape playback machine was devised which would play a short sequence of sounds as many times a minute and as many minutes in the day as was desirable. In the first experiments an artificial song of very pure tonal quality was used, a quality thought to be rather similar to that pro-duced by a bird flageolet. Attempts to teach Chaffinches this song failed. Subsequent experience points to the conclusion that this was because the song, while reasonably correct in pitch, duration and number of notes, was completely abnormal in tonal quality, the notes having far too pure and flute-like a timbre. It seems then that the Chaffinch is strikingly different from some other finches in regard to the kind of sound to which it will pay attention and will copy. The next step, therefore, was

[1] A process by which, as soon as they can walk, young animals (especially the young of nidifugous birds) learn to recognise the appearance of their own species by following their parents.

to take Chaffinch songs, normal and abnormal, and use these on the song-tutor machine and subsequently to modify them in various ways for purposes of experiment. The experiments carried out in the 1954–5 season with four wild Chaffinches given tuition consisting of the songs of a normal Chaffinch in the late

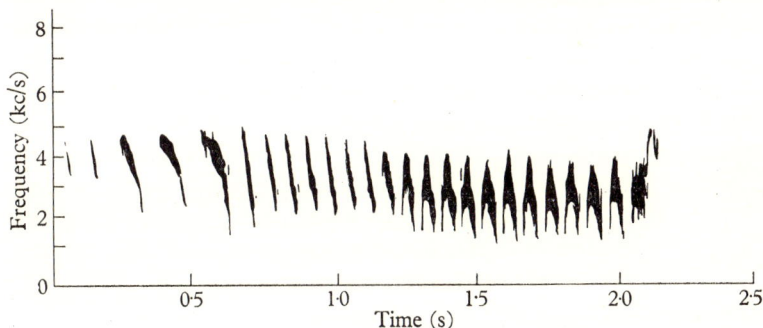

Fig. 42. Chaffinch. Effect on song of auditory Kaspar Hauser bird of tutoring with normal song. The song of the Kaspar Hauser is nearing normality. (Thorpe, 1958a.)

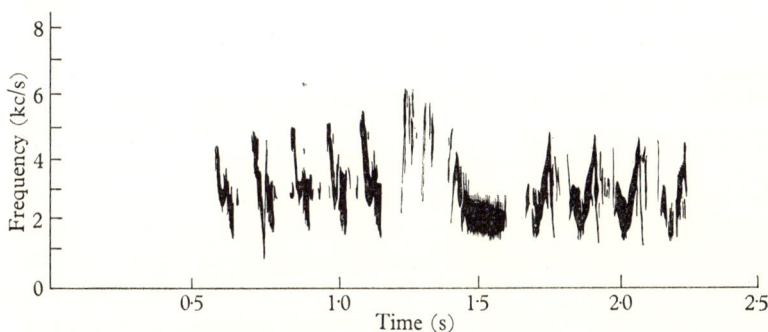

Fig. 43. Chaffinch, re-articulated song produced for tutoring. End transferred to middle. (Thorpe, 1958a.)

winter and in February and March showed some effect of the song-tutor. With hand-reared birds the results were much clearer. Fig. 42 gives an example of this. More abnormal models were then supplied to the birds, either by playing a song backwards or by cutting it up into sections and interchanging the sections, producing, for instance, a song with the ending transferred to the middle (see fig. 43). Songs produced in this way were, of course, very abnormal, by Chaffinch standards, and it is interesting to note that whereas they had little or no effect on Chaffinches caught as young birds in the autumn, they were readily learned by hand-reared Chaffinches which had not had the autumnal experience normal for the species. It seems the former birds had already learned enough about normal Chaffinch song to prevent them copying these highly abnormal models. Fig. 47 shows a Chaffinch copy of the model, in which the end had been transferred to the middle.

These experiments suggested that the Chaffinches were not likely to learn alien bird-song from our song-tutor any more than they learn alien songs in the wild, and it was therefore decided that if an alien song was used at all, it must be one which obviously approximated in tonal quality to the Chaffinch song. Inspection of sound spectrograms confirmed conclusions based on the unaided ear, that the song of the Tree Pipit was probably tonally nearer to the Chaffinch than that of any other common British bird. The continental form of the Tree Pipit's song was used as a model (fig. 44). Figs. 45 and 46 show the version of this Tree Pipit song produced by a hand-reared Chaffinch R/R as a result of hearing it on a tape for three periods of a fortnight each in January, March and April 1956. This song is quite unlike any other song ever produced in my experience by a wild or hand-reared Chaffinch and it is of interest to note that the rather long song of the model, which was over 3 s, has been condensed to conform to the standard length of Chaffinch song by condensing the middle phrase of the Tree Pipit song to two notes instead of four. The second figure shows the final result of this tightening up process as heard in May 1956. It is interesting that in the following season, 1957, this bird dropped its Tree Pipit song and produced only a modified version of its innate or Kaspar Hauser song.

The wide frequency-range of the individual notes of the subsong as compared with those of the full song has already been referred to. So at least some part of the process of changing subsong into full song consists in discarding those more extreme frequencies which are not required in the latter. The process is one which suggests, at least superficially, the theory of some students of human speech that the young baby makes, during the course of many months' experimentation with its own vocal apparatus, every conceivable sound which that apparatus is capable of producing. It thus has the raw material, so to speak,

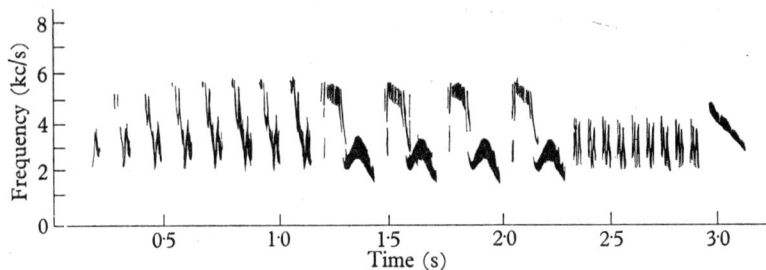

Fig. 44. Continental Tree Pipit, *Anthus t. trivialis*, used as a model on song tutor. (Thorpe, 1958*a*.)

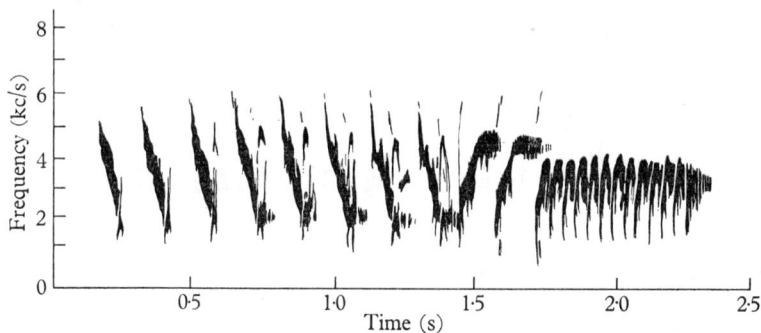

Fig. 45. Chaffinch. Song of hand-reared auditory Kaspar Hauser bird after tutoring for three periods with Tree Pipit song. (Thorpe, 1958*a*.)

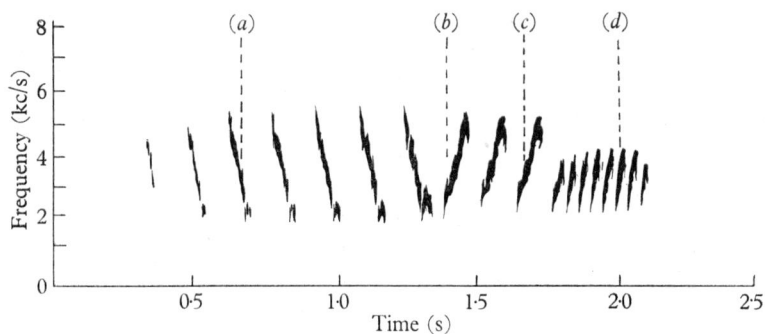

Fig. 46. Improved Tree Pipit song produced by the same Chaffinch as in fig. 45 after further period of practice. (Thorpe, 1958*a*.)

83

whatever its race or colour, for speaking all the languages of the world. But as the child grows up it pays more and more attention to the sounds it hears from its parents and other adults around and tends gradually to drop out those sounds which have no part in the speech of its family. Thus there is no indication (apart possibly from the ability to pronounce 'th' sounds) that human children start with any inborn ability to speak a particular language, but that very early they become conditioned, by elimination and imitation, to the language of their environment. So it also appears to be, at any rate in some degree, with the Chaffinch; except that the Chaffinch has the

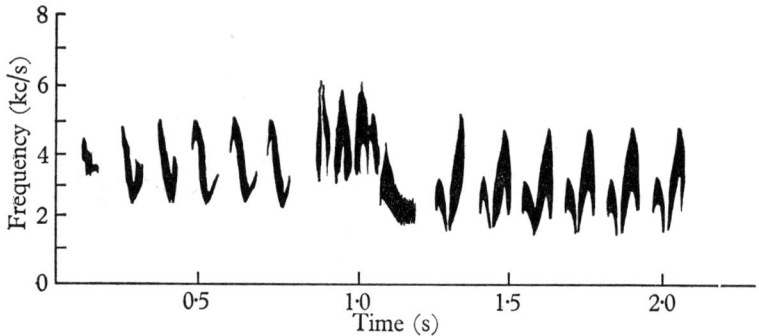

Fig. 47. Chaffinch. Song of hand-reared auditory Kaspar Hauser bird after having been exposed to re-articulated song, with end in middle, on song tutor for 12 days January–February and 12 days February–March 1958. Compare with model, fig. 43. (Thorpe, 1958 *b*.)

inborn blueprint conferring on it a tendency to learn to pay attention to certain kinds of sounds and certain types of phrase only, and thus incline it to learn songs of the Chaffinch rather than any other kind of vocalisation. Thus the later stages of the subsong do appear to be a kind of practice for the future full song. It is also worthy of note that while the pitch of the full song is so constant throughout life as to suggest that the bird 'has absolute pitch' (though never so precisely as a gifted human has it), this pitch may be lower when the same individual song-pattern is still in its developmental stage as part of the subsong. Though the Chaffinch is not an imitative species, there are a number of cases of Chaffinches including in their subsong, but not in their full song, call-notes and other sounds produced by other species. These include Great Tit, Hedge Sparrow, Goldcrest, Coal Tit and Greenfinch. The same phenomenon was evident in the experiments with the song-tutor: the Chaffinches used sometimes learned to incorporate in their subsong phrases which were far more abnormal in tonal quality and structure than anything which they could normally be induced to include in their full songs. Thus a hand-reared Chaffinch successfully produced

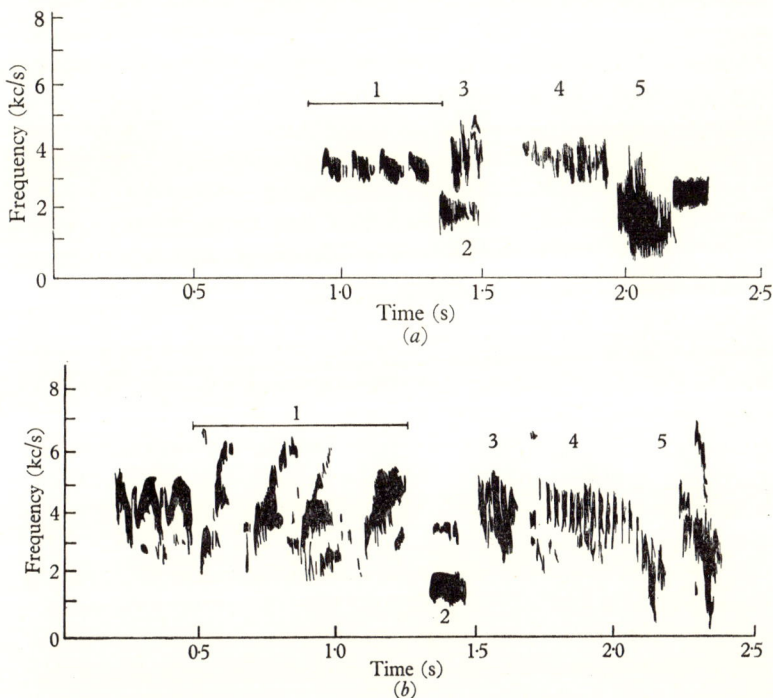

Fig. 48. Imitation of canary song by Chaffinch in its subsong. (a) Phrase in subsong of Chaffinch exposed to canary song; (b) canary song on which Chaffinch song (a) was modelled. (Thorpe, 1958a.)

a rough imitation of a reversed song in its subsong, but this was apparently too abnormal to admit of its being used in the full song on more than about 3 per cent of singing occasions. Figs. 48a and b show the inclusion by a young Chaffinch in its subsong, quite unexpectedly and apparently without rehearsal, of a phrase of canary song to which it had been exposed some weeks previously. Nevertheless, when this bird came eventually to produce its full song, it sedulously avoided contaminating it with the canary notes previously learned, and its full song (it having been an isolated bird) was of the simple Kaspar Hauser type. Results such as this serve to emphasise the distinction between subsong and full song and suggest the conclusion that, because of its importance as a territorial proclamation and as a specific recognition mark, full song must be kept pure and uncontaminated, whereas the subsong, being functionless in communication, can be the vehicle of playful imitation of no immediate consequence, but possibly facilitating the later acquisition of full song. The work of Lanyon (1957) and Poulsen (1959) shows the situation in the Meadow Lark and the domestic canary to be remarkably similar.

When a male Chaffinch has more than one song-type in its repertoire, each song outburst consists of a sequence of one song-type followed by a sequence of another. Hinde (1958) made a special study of this, using Chaffinches which had been taught two or more very different songs, one of which was more or less unmodified isolate song. These songs were played back to the Chaffinches, and the type of song to which they responded was noted. It was found that the alternations of song-types in an outburst of singing can be largely understood in terms of the competing self-inhibitory and self-facilitating effect of each song-type on its own repetition. When songs are played back to a Chaffinch those song-types which it uses most frequently itself are most effective in evoking singing, irrespective of whether they resemble normal song or not. Although the learning of the motor pattern of song and of the receptory mechanism whereby a song is responded to could be separate processes, this result suggests that they depend on the same initial stage—namely, the acquisition of a selective responsiveness to the stimulus song. Thus when a Chaffinch is singing against other Chaffinches in neighbouring territories it will, if these experimental results hold good under natural conditions, tend to reply with that song in its repertoire which most nearly resembles the song of its rival. When a song from a given Chaffinch's repertoire is played back to it repeatedly, the frequency of that type of song in its singing-bouts increases. Thus it may be that the ability of a Chaffinch to reply to a neighbouring male defending a nearby territory with the kind of song which that male itself is singing may be recognised by the rival as a more effective, a more threatening territorial-defence mechanism than if the song it replied with was independent of the song it had just heard. So it may be that a bird responding to a rival in this way can be said to be 'giving as good as it gets'.

The next question is, how far does this story apply to other species? It is a widely known fact that different species of birds vary greatly in their song-learning ability. Among European finches we find that the best at learning alien songs are those, such as the Bullfinch, and Greenfinch, of which the songs seem to be much less important as a territorial proclamation than is that of the Chaffinch. Indeed the songs of many of these finches recall the subsong rather than the full song of the Chaffinch. Following up this idea, one is led to the conclusion that these songs may be mainly concerned with co-ordinating the breeding-cycle and behaviour of a mated pair. If this is so, we have at least a possible reason why such songs could remain flexible without endangering the process of territory establishment and the breeding-cycle which follows from it. As Marler (1960) suggests, if the song is concerned in maintaining a pair bond which lasts for a number of seasons, individual recognition may be important and variation will be encouraged. Similarly, physiological synchronisation might be better effected by variation than by stereotypy. Certainly most, if not all, of our British finches are better mimics than is the Chaffinch, and the long-established training-schools for Bullfinches in Germany show that this was well known to the aviculturalists of the last century. There is some evidence to suggest that hybrid finches may be more adept at learning alien songs than are either of the parent species. We have now for a number of years kept most species of British finches in outdoor aviaries at the Madingley Field Station and by far the most striking imitative performance yet observed was that (fig. 49) in which a Goldfinch × Greenfinch hybrid learned to produce an almost perfect Chaffinch song as a result of hearing a Chaffinch singing repeatedly just outside its aviary. Why this should be is not clear, but it is possible that the breakdown and confusion of the innate song-pattern resulting from hybridisation allows the imitative ability greater scope, so that the hybrids tend to be less restricted as to the models which they will adopt for learning. A hybrid Brambling × Chaffinch, however, produced normal Chaffinch song although Bramblings being numerous in adjacent aviaries were even more available as song models than Chaffinches.

There is at present little evidence as to how far this picture

87

of the development of song obtained from a study of the Chaffinch applies to other species. Nicolai, in his intensive study of the Bullfinch, was almost completely unsuccessful in his attempt to find a function for the song in this species. Nevertheless, there is a good deal of vocal imitation and his work (1959) provides the only example so far of a family tradition in song, the young bird singing like its parent and grandparent. The song-development of a number of species of buntings has been studied in a preliminary fashion. The full songs of buntings are loud, phasic and oft repeated—characteristics which suggest that they are in general of territorial importance. They are also strongly stereotyped and specific, but nevertheless in the Song

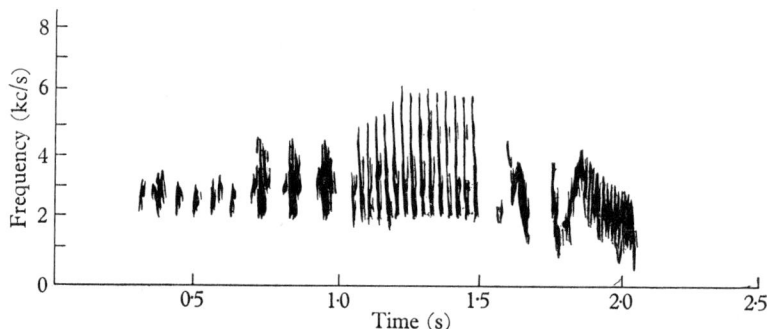

Fig. 49. Imitation of Chaffinch song by hybrid Goldfinch × Greenfinch, 28 April 1955. (Thorpe, 1958a.)

Sparrow, at least, the situation resembles the Chaffinch in that there is a great deal of individual variation within the limits of the specific pattern. We have reared one or two individuals of three species of British buntings in auditory isolation from the early nestling stage—the Corn Bunting, the Reed Bunting and the Yellow Bunting. In the first two species the songs of the isolates were indistinguishable from those of wild birds. With the Yellow Bunting and Cirl Bunting, however, the existence of local and individual song-variants similar to those of the Chaffinch is known, and observation on the former species suggest that possibly the component parts of the song in the Yellow Bunting are innate, but that the ending cannot be attached in the normal manner without some learning, a situation resembling that in the Chaffinch, and also described in the Blackbird (Thielcke-Poltz and Thielcke, 1960).

But although the function of imitation when it is restricted to the singer's own species is plausible enough, it is very difficult to find an adequate explanation of the extreme imitativeness of some well-known mimics such as the Mockingbird, the mynahs and some other members of the Sturnidae. There has been a good deal of discussion as to how much mimicry the Mockingbird actually achieves. Loye Miller provided evidence that about 10 per cent of the song of the species was copied from other species. Later work, however, suggested that it is much higher than this. Thus Borror and Reese (1959) mention 102 songs of Mockingbirds in their collection which they consider sufficiently similar to the songs of the Carolina Wren to be termed imitation. They do not, however, give particulars of the total number of Mockingbird recordings from which these 102 songs were selected. Their sound-spectrographic records, nevertheless, seem to leave no doubt that true imitation is taking place in this species to a very large extent. They state that in spite of all their recordings and all their audio-spectrographic equipment, they have the feeling that the Mockingbirds have a much better knowledge of the song-patterns of Carolina Wrens than they have.

Marshall (1950) points out that most vocal mimics in Australia (for example, lyre birds) are strongly territorial, and most of them carry out much of their mimicry in song near the ground in wooded country where visibility is limited. He suggests, therefore, that the lack of visibility places a premium on communication by sound and that it is biologically advantageous for individuals to make more and more sound in order that territorial rivals and members of the opposite sex shall be constantly aware of their presence. This argument seems a rather doubtful one, however: it is not necessary for a bird to be imitative in order to make plenty of noise, and making a loud and persistent noise will not avail the species at all unless that noise is recognised as a specific signal by other birds. Only if—as is perhaps the case—the vocal quality is such that the species is recognisable *whatever* song-pattern it utters, would mimicry of this kind seem to be biologically permissible. But even if the vocal quality is recognisable, that does not of itself seem to suggest any advantage to a bird in declaiming the song-patterns of others rather than of its own species—although it might be an easy way of increasing the individual character of a bird's song, since no two birds are likely to copy the same model in the same way or sequence.

Finally, we come to the vexed problem of inventiveness in song, a problem that was touched upon in the first chapter. Musical 'invention' includes (a) rearrangement of phrases, both innate and learned, and (b) the invention of really 'new' material. It appears, for instance, that individuals of the Blackbird (Messmer and Messmer, 1956), the Sprosser Nightingale (Sotovalta, 1956) and the Shama (Thorpe, in progress) do produce new songs by the combination of phrases they have used before, some of which are inherited, others probably learned—certainly so in the case of the Shama. The Messmers found that the young in their first spring learn entire patterns or parts of their songs from adults. During the winter these motifs are incorporated into a juvenile song, and the next spring they form the first song-pattern. Birds of the third brood do not acquire their first patterns until after the winter. Thus Blackbirds are able to adopt patterns from their neighbours in a short time. In spring new compositions suddenly occur amongst the learned patterns. In this way each male obtains a repertoire of five to seven patterns and the young birds sing a number of variations of their motifs. As with the Chaffinch, this species shows evidence of having innate bases of song-pattern and of building up and elaborating these by a process of learning, including imitation. Hall-Craggs (1961, in the press) has followed out in close detail the development of song in some wild Blackbird individuals and gives some striking examples of the development and elaboration of phrases to an extent which seems to suggest something similar to real musical invention. Fig. 50 shows characteristic examples of her work. Marler (1959) gives similar evidence for Mistle Thrush and Song Thrush. The extent of the repertoire to which such a method can lead is astonishing. Thus Marler mentions a Robin which performed a series of fifty-seven songs, every one of which was different, and with Song and Mistle Thrush the number may be nearly as great. Borror (1956) reports a Carolina Wren singing twenty-two different songs in twenty-four bursts of singing.

While it is convenient to distinguish between reorganisation and new invention, the two categories are not completely separable. Thus even the Chaffinch, especially the hand-reared bird, certainly shows some invention. Moreover, in the Song

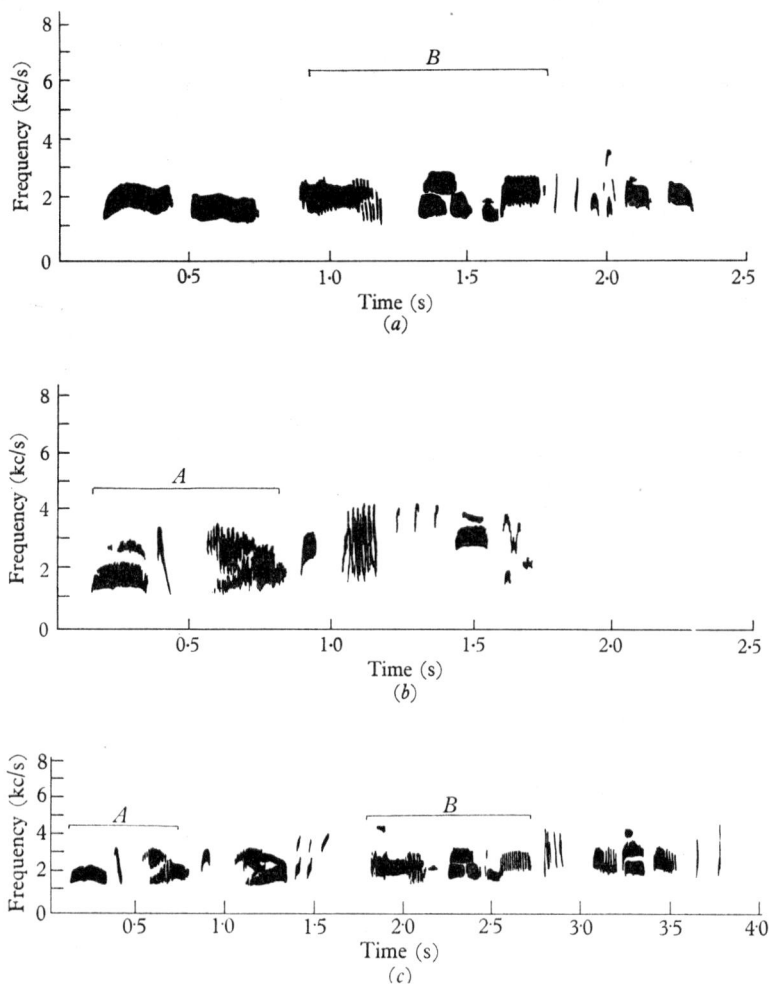

Fig. 50. Records of song development in a single wild Blackbird, showing the development and elaboration of an end phrase, suggesting musical invention. (a) Phrase 4; (b) phrase 17, (c) phrase 17/4, which includes parts of phrases 4 and 17. (Hall-Craggs, 1961.)

Sparrow and some of the other buntings, even though all the main elements of the song are innate, distinguishable differences can be produced by slight consistent variation in the duration of the different notes, the duration of phrases (that is, the spacing of the notes) and in relative pitch and emphasis during the course of the song; so it is really impossible to say where rearrangement stops and new inventions begin. Even within the restriction imposed by an entirely innate song, therefore, there is a good deal of raw material for individual characteristics to develop. Where the song is long and the number of innate phrases great, then there will be still further possibilities for individual variation in that the phrases themselves can be rearranged. Thus differences have been noted which are based on the frequency with which particular phrases are interposed. Sound spectrographic studies have shown that where the song is phasic and repeated in short bursts, as in the Mistle Thrush, the result strikes the casual listener as monotonous and we are apt to conclude that there is very little difference from one individual to the next. But on closer inspection one finds that there is in fact much more variation than one would have thought but that this variation occurs particularly in the first few notes of each phrase, the final notes being relatively stereotyped. The ordinary listener subconsciously pays much more attention to the final notes and so gets a false impression of monotony.

CHAPTER 6

Specific and Sub-specific Differences in Vocalisation

IN this chapter it is proposed to consider the value of songs and call-notes as systematic characters, and their biological significance as individual recognition marks. It is so obvious as hardly to need saying that vocal quality often provides a fairly good sub-ordinal or familial characteristic: ducks quack, doves coo, owls hoot or screech, etc. These characteristics may very well often be dependent upon gross anatomical features of the vocal-organs, although it is surprising, when one comes to look into the matter, how flimsy is the evidence upon this point (see chapter 7).

Within the Passeriformes, however, the voice is of very little use in the task of diagnosing the major systematic categories; and where it may have such value, as perhaps in the Turdidae (Marler, 1959), the resemblances cannot be related to any known anatomical features. Although the differentiation of Passeriformes into oscines and others is a convenience, it does not emphasise any quality of voice which could be used for broad classificatory purposes. Even the most primitive passeriform group, the broad-bills (Eurylaimidae), whilst hardly producing anything that could be called a song, have notes which would not disgrace many of the families of the oscines. Descending from the categories of order and suborder to that of family and genus, we find again that vocal characters are of extremely limited systematic value. In fact the reasons for the limitations of the usefulness of vocal characters for categories above that of species are not very hard to find. As Marler (1955, 1959, 1960) points out, there are many groups of birds in which songs, while providing extremely good specific differences, are almost useless in defining the higher categories. This is understandable, for if song functions in reproductive isolation by attracting and stimulating a mate, the songs are likely to be highly divergent between two closely allied sympatric species. In such cases there will have been intense selection for specific distinctiveness; but, conversely, similarity between the songs within a genus would confer no evolutionary advantage at all—in fact it is more likely to be dysgenic. The very fact that so many bird-songs and other vocalisations are in some way involved in reproductive isolation means that they are likely to be highly divergent between closely allied sympatric species. They will therefore be useful as characters for specific diagnosis; but of course the very fact of their having been selected for specific distinctiveness means that any generic or familial similarity which may originally have been present will have been masked, reduced or eliminated in the course of evolution (Marler, 1957). An interesting partial exception to this generalisation is provided by the subfamily Estrildinae of the family Ploceidae. There are three major divisions or tribes in the subfamily: the waxbills (Estrildae), the grass finches (Erythrurae) and the manakins (Amadinae). Delacour (1943) points out that the Estrildae all have high-pitched chirping or sweet calls and song, much like the true cardueline finches, and that they utter them beak upwards. The Erythrurae have unmelodious voices— clucking, mournful, trumpeting, metallic or low, but never sweet, chirping and finch-like. The Amadinae are harder to characterise by voice alone than the other tribes, the voice in general being like that of the grass finches, but clucking or trumpeting sounds are very characteristic and their song-dance is more static, with a ventriloquial quality very much in evidence. Marler, however, has pointed out that the songs of the Estrildinae probably do not have an advertising function and that they are often very soft, and audible only at close range. It follows that they may thus be free of the demands of extreme specific distinctiveness. Moreover, if the main function of song is to repel rivals rather than attract mates, some relaxation of characteristics for specific distinctiveness will occur, since it will not matter if other species are repelled too (Marler, 1960).

When we come to consider vocalisations as specific characters the case is so obvious that again there is very little to say, but for a different reason, since it is hard to find closely related sympatric species-pairs among the song birds which are not obviously differentiated immediately one hears their songs. Indeed when we consider the subfamily Sylviinae of the western palearctic region, which includes some thirty species of the birds usually known as warblers, there are only two species-pairs which come obviously to mind as being hard to distinguish in the field by vocal characteristics. These are the Blackcap and Garden Warbler (Sauer 1955) and the Savi's Warbler (*Locustella luscinoides*) and Grasshopper Warbler (*Locustella naevia*) (Thorpe,

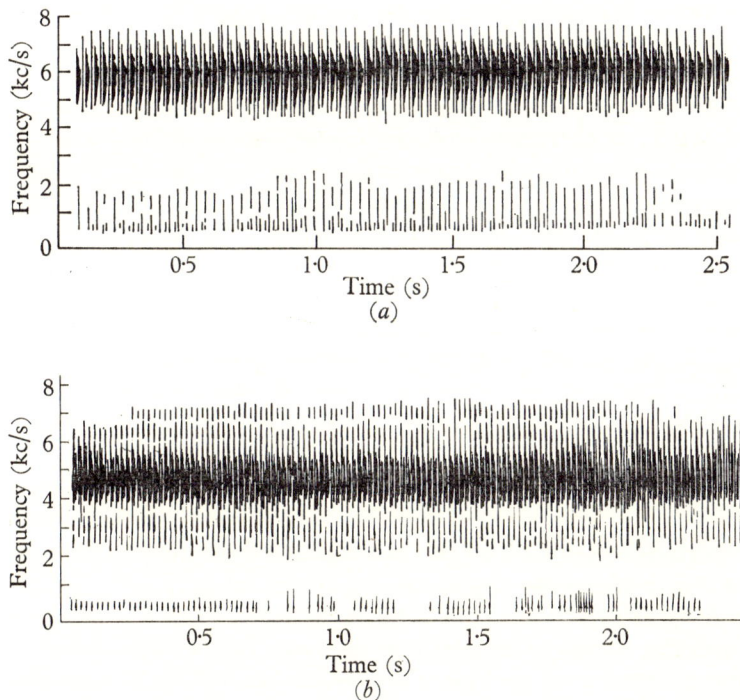

Fig. 51. Songs of (*a*) Grasshopper Warbler; (*b*) Savi's Warbler. (*a*) has thirty-one triple pulses per second with an energy peak at 5 kc, whilst the closely related species (*b*) has about fifty double pulses per second with energy peaks at 2 and 4 kc.

1957; Broughton, *in litt.*). Even in these critical species, however, the birds can be distinguished vocally with some degree of reliability and indeed there are some field-naturalists who feel quite confident that they can separate them by hearing alone under any reasonably good conditions. However this may be, a study of the recordings so far available makes it quite clear that there are in fact good vocal characters which no doubt the birds can appreciate even if human beings cannot do so. Thus analysis

95

reveals that *naevia* has thirty-one triple pulses per second, with an energy peak at 5 kc/s, whereas *luscinioides* has about fifty double pulses per second with energy peaks at 2 and 4 kc/s. The triple pulses of *naevia*, when studied oscillographically, show some harsh transients which are lacking in the double pulses of *luscinioides*. This, so far as it goes, would confirm the general conclusion of German field-ornithologists (see Voigt, 11th edn., 1950) who say that *naevia* 'rattles' (*klirren*), while *luscinioides* 'buzzes' (*schnurren*) (see fig. 51). It is interesting that the fact that *luscinioides* has peaks at 2 and 4 kc—which is about the frequency of top C of the piano and the C one octave below—and the fact that it lacks the transients fits in with Eliot Howard's impression that the song of *luscinioides* is far more musical than that of *naevia* and in a way resembles 'the tinkling of tiny numerous bells'. The energy peak of *naevia* at 5 kc, that is, considerably above the top note of the piano, would probably not strike most human ears as musical and even without the transients would probably be sufficient to account for the difference in impression they give to the human listener. Dr Broughton tells me that in records which he has analysed oscillographically there is some evidence that the pulses of *naevia* are still further divided. If this is so, it may indicate some very high-frequency components well beyond the range of recorders which have so far been used on these birds. The study of this genus with apparatus recording up to 100 kc/s might well be worth trying. The song of the River Warbler, *Locustella fluviatilis*, is also of remarkable interest. To the human ear its notes sound loud and clear and much more clearly separated than either of the other two species. This is in line with the fact that the bursts of sound occur at the rate of 12–15/s, each lasting about $\frac{1}{20}$ s. Thus at first sight the song appears to resemble the song of *luscinioides* greatly slowed down. In actual fact further analysis suggests that the song of *fluviatilis* is speeded up and not slowed down, since each pulse of 20 s duration seems to comprise about twelve constituent pulses, the repetition rate of the elements in the train being about 250/s. If this is the correct interpretation the whole song of *fluviatilis* is really one order higher—that is to say it is a sequence of songs at the rate of 12/s. Incidentally, the pulse repetition rate of 250/s poses physiological questions analogous to those raised by the utterances of bats and perhaps some cave birds. Summing up the matter, although Savi's Warbler and the Grasshopper Warbler appear at first hearing to be only very doubtfully distinguishable by sound characters alone, the evidence now suggests that their vocal characteristics will prove as reliable diagnostically as those of any other similar species-pairs. It seems probable that they do not provide an exception to Ernst Mayr's dictum that there do not exist, either in Europe or North America, any species-pairs which are not distinguishable on the basis of song (Mayr, 1956).

Where one member of a species-pair has spread into another continent and started evolution there, it sometimes happens that the song remains surprisingly constant, providing dramatic evidence for the instinctive nature of some bird-songs and showing that, in contrast to the racial differentiation of songs (to be discussed below), the song-pattern may remain extraordinarily stereotyped over a long period of time if there is no selective reason for its differentiation. Thus if we compare the song of the roller canary, bred for song characters for many generations, with that of the border canary, bred for appearance, and with that of the wild canary in its ancestral home in the Canary Islands, we find that the only difference between the last two lies in the disappearance, in the border canary, of some dissonant notes in the first half of the song of the wild bird. The roller canary song, however, sounds quite different as a result of a change towards a lower pitch, a simpler or more repetitive structure, and shorter intervals between notes (fig. 52) (Marler, 1959). Similarly, the British and Tenerife forms of both the Corn Bunting and the Blackbird have almost exactly similar songs. Again, when we come to compare the songs of European and North American representatives of certain species, we find some very striking examples. Thus Mayr (1956) records that R. T. Peterson finds far greater differences between the populations of the European Wren *Troglodytes t. troglodytes*, in Europe, than between *T. t. troglodytes* and the corresponding American species, *T. t. hiemalis*, the Winter Wren.[1] The difference between the songs of these two species has been shown to be chiefly one of length, the American Winter Wren having a song about twice as long as that of the European Wren, and consisting

---

[1] E. A. Armstrong (personal communication) who has a wider field knowledge of the species than any other naturalist, strongly dissents from this opinion.

fundamentally of the song of the European Wren twice over (see Armstrong, 1955). In the case of the Treecreepers, the American, *Certhia americana*, had been thought to be a representative of the European species *brachydactyla*; but the vocalisation of *americana* is so close to the European *familiaris* that there

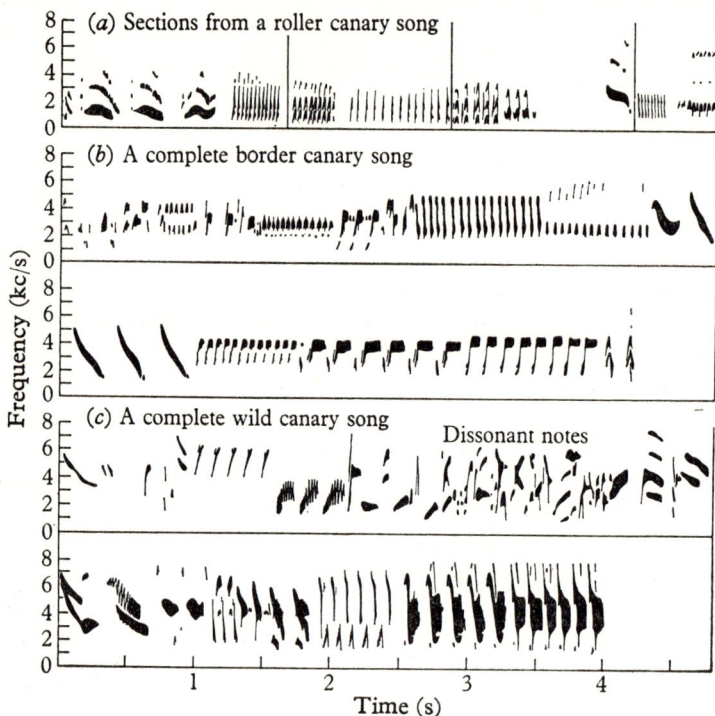

Fig. 52. Samples from the song of the roller canary, bred for song characters, the border canary bred for appearance, and the wild canary recorded in the Canary Islands. Note similarity of songs of wild and border canary except for the disappearance of the dissonant notes in the first half of the wild bird's song. Roller canary song has been changed towards a lower pitch, a simpler and more repetitive structure and shorter intervals between notes. (Marler, 1959.)

can be little doubt that *americana* should be regarded as a race of *familiaris*, not of *brachydactyla*. One final example among those supplied by Mayr is cited to show how cautiously these characteristics must be used. The American Black-capped Chickadee, *Parus atricapillus*, has a song so similar to that of the European Willow Tit, *P. montanus salicarius*, that an ornithologist fresh from Europe, on hearing the American species would immediately say 'typical Willow Tit'. However, a study of the races of *P. atricapillus* in America shows that although it is undoubtedly nearer to *montanus* than to the European Marsh Tit, *P. palustris*, it cannot be conspecific with either but is correctly regarded as a distinct species. Another corrective to any undue tendency to rely upon vocal characteristics for specific definition is provided by the Golden-winged and Blue-winged Warblers, *Vermivora chrysoptera* and *V. pinus*. These two species are undoubtedly closely related and are distinct in plumage. Their simple songs are very similar to one another, though unlike those of any other warbler, but the differences are normally sufficient for identification. It has, however, been recorded that both species occasionally sing the song of the other (Peterson, 1934). A similar state of affairs has been reported in the European Tree Creepers (Thielcke, 1960).

It is well known that in many cases the song of the species can be sufficiently constant and distinct to serve as a specific recognition mark, but yet can vary within these limits sufficiently to indicate subspecific, racial and local populations. A number of examples of subspecific vocal characteristics are given by Mayr (1942), Stanford (1945) and Benson (1948). The last-named's evidence is particularly interesting since it is based on very wide experience throughout Africa. He describes thirty-three instances of local variation, mostly of small degree, out of over 200 species studied, many of which were allopatric pairs. Chapman (1940) gives particulars of differences in the song of various races of *Zonotrichia capensis*. One of the most isolated of these, *Z. capensis antillarum*, from San Dominica, has a song resembling a *Melospiza*, which is very different from that of any other *Z. capensis* race. *Capensis* is a Central and South American species, but similarly the White-crowned Sparrow in California, *Z. leucophrys*, has different community song-patterns in different regions, these probably being of a phenotypic nature—that is to say, local traditions (Peterson, 1941). The Spanish Chiffchaff provides a borderline case. It was formerly given subspecific rank as *Phylloscopus collybita ibericus*, but is now (Vaurie, 1959) included under the nominate race. Ticehurst (1938) described its song as entirely unlike that of any other European races of *P. collybita*. The Eastern and Western Meadowlarks, *Sturnella m. magna* and *S. m. neglecta*, have often been cited as subspecies differentiated by song. While this may be true on the average, the careful work of Lanyon (1957) seems to show that while call-notes may offer a reliable differentiation, song does not. Witherby, Jourdain, Ticehurst and Tucker (1948) report that in one locality in Lapland all or nearly all the Redwings sang the same stereotyped phrase whilst only thirty miles away all sang quite differently. Marshall (1950) reports local variation in the advertisement call of *Ptilonorhynchus*, the Australian bower-birds. Other species in which geographical trends in vocalisation have been intensively studied include the Carolina Wren (Borror, 1956) and the Rufous-sided Towhee (Borror, 1959). Other examples of local communities of a species, each having a characteristic song-pattern, are given by Mayr (1956), Marler (1960, pp. 352–4) and are also described by Linsdale (1928) for the Fox Sparrow, Saunders (1951) for the Song Sparrow, and Slud (1958) for the Nightingale Wren in Costa Rica. The songs of the British Chaffinch (*Fringilla coelebs gengleri*), whilst showing average differences from one locality to another, do not display any real geographical trends (Thorpe, 1958a). Similarly, there is no absolutely constant character distinguishing the song of the British Chaffinch from that of the Continental Chaffinch, *F. c. coelebs*. Here again we can see no definite geographical trend, but *coelebs* has the last note made up of pulses of about 0·012 s duration, whereas only two of the twenty-one recorded songs of *gengleri* show this structure.

Not only may the same individual Chaffinch have two or more distinct songs, but these songs may be different in almost every detail. Five birds, caught as juveniles in Cambridge, were kept with other Chaffinches in aviaries where they could hear many Chaffinches, both wild and aviary birds, in full song. There are only two features in which the songs of these birds resemble one another: (1) they are of almost the same total length, (2) the final phrases tend to match (this perhaps being simply an expression of conformation to the general local tradition as illustrated by the birds all around them). These differences in the Chaffinch song are individually characteristic and once a bird has completed its first season as an adult, that is, as soon as it is fourteen months old, its song or songs have become stereotyped and the experienced ear can thereafter recognise a given bird with almost complete certainty, as by a signature tune. The establishment of local dialects in the Chaffinch is not confined to song. In the continental race, *F. c.*

coelebs, the *huit* alarm call is much more variable than in *gengleri* and may form double or even polysyllabic notes of very different timbre. Some such forms, rarely heard in England, are known on the Continent as the 'rain call' in a belief that they foretell a change in the weather. Sick (1939) has described a mosaic of very small 'dialect areas' in the Stuttgart region, where the boundaries may be nothing more prominent than a road or a railway yet *appear* to remain stable over many generations. It is plausibly presumed that these are true dialects and are not based on genetic discontinuities. Marler has described similar highly localised dialects in the Azores.

The Chaffinch is apparently now firmly established in an extremely restricted area of Cape Town and its suburbs,

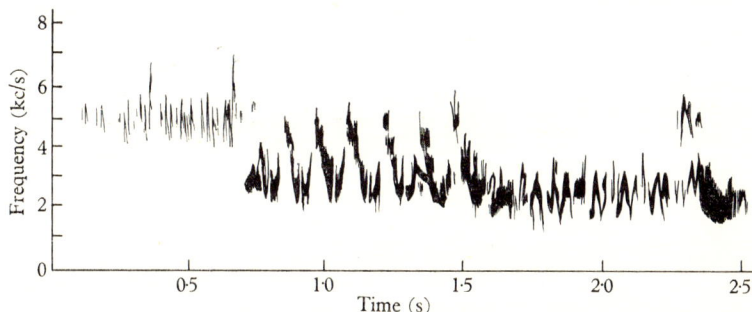

Fig. 53. Song of a Chaffinch from Newlands, Cape Town, South Africa, September 1957. (G. J. Broekhuysen, from Thorpe, 1958*a*.) The Chaffinch was introduced to South Africa in 1900.

not larger than twelve square miles, and has never spread further. Observers in South Africa say that they do not notice much local variation in the song; but this would hardly be expected with a population of such limited distribution unless broken up by ecological barriers. I am greatly indebted to Dr Broekhuysen for obtaining a recording of what appeared to him to be some characteristic songs of one individual of the Cape Town population (fig. 53) and fig. 54 shows a Chaffinch song from New Zealand where the species has been established since 1862. They are seen to be full-length songs, the division into three phrases being very obvious. All except phrase 1 *a* might be regarded as normal for *gengleri*. It is not known whether the Chaffinches at present wild in South Africa and New Zealand can be definitely assigned to *gengleri* or *coelebs*; Dr J. M. Winterbottom recently brought me a freshly prepared skin from South Africa, but comparison with the series in the British Museum (Natural History) leaves the problem still unsolved.

The songs of outlying subspecies of the Chaffinch have been observed by Marler and Boatman (1951) and Marler (1956). Though no recordings are available, the Chaffinch in the Azores, *F. c. moreleti*, and that in the Canary Islands *F. c. tintillon*, certainly have, on the whole, simpler songs than those characteristic of either *gengleri* or *coelebs*. Of twenty-eight examples heard by Marler and Boatman on Pico (Azores),

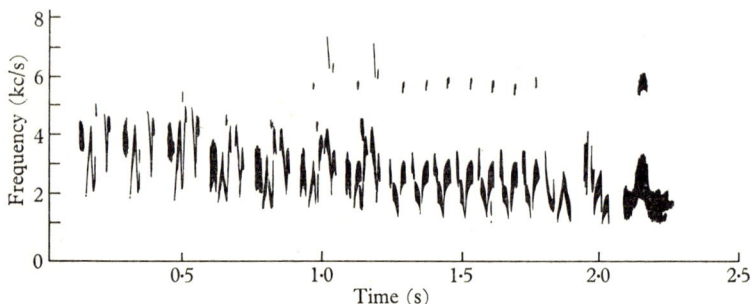

Fig. 54. Typical song of a Chaffinch from New Zealand, where the species was introduced in 1862. Recorded by Kenneth and Jean Bigwood.

none had an elaborate phrase 3*b* and phrase 3*a* was lacking altogether or represented merely by a single note. Examples were heard in which phrases 1*a*, 1*b* and 2 could be distinguished, and these probably represent the characteristic Azores Chaffinch song, although a type (apparently very similar to that of a *coelebs* or *gengleri* raised in isolation) in which 1*a*, 1*b* and 2 consisted of a simple undifferentiated descending series of notes was observed in sixteen out of twenty-five examples. The Madeiran Chaffinch, *F. c. maderensis*, and the Canary race *F. c. tintillon*, are each characteristic of the laurel forests of their respective islands. The first, recorded in aviaries at Madingley, produced a song similar to *coelebs* but lacking the normal ending. It is not as simple as that of *tintillon* which apparently is nearer to *F. teydea* than to *coelebs*.

The Blue Chaffinch, *Fringilla teydea*, occurs only on the island of Tenerife, where it is restricted to the pine forests. We also had this bird in our aviaries at Madingley and Dr Marler has also studied it in its native habitat. Its characteristic song is shown in Fig. 55. It will be seen that again, compared with the European bird, the song is simple, phrase 1 having five notes and phrase 2 only two, but nevertheless the song is not far short of the normal length. The pitch is low, varying between 1 and 4 kc. It is in fact almost exactly like several examples of the song of Kaspar Hauser *F. c. gengleri*.

The work of Promptoff on the song of *F. c. coelebs* in two localities in Moscow and the West Urals has been summarised by Marler (1952). It seems that the song of the Russian birds is similar to the western European form as regards phrases 1

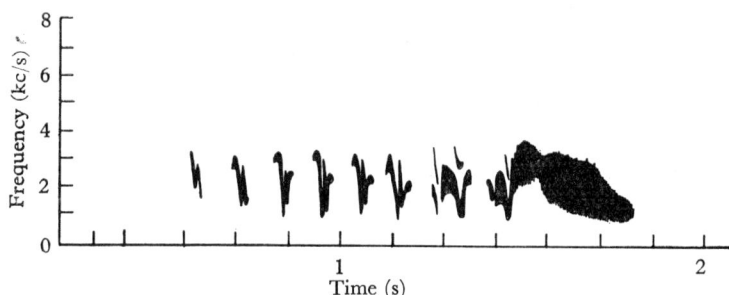

Fig. 55. Song of Blue Chaffinch, *Fringilla teydea*, on Tenerife.
(Marler, 1959.)

and 2, but that the range of notes in the phrases is lower and that the mean number of notes per phrase is also lower— 1·99 from Russia as compared with 2·91 from western Europe. These latter figures include some *coelebs* but are composed mainly of *gengleri*.

Lack and Southern (1949) were the first to draw attention to the possibility that difference in bird-song between the populations of the same species in the crowded avifauna of continental Europe and in the smaller and more sparse avifauna of the Atlantic islands, such as Tenerife, might be explained by the reduction in selection pressure for specific distinctiveness in the latter environment. This seems to be borne out by present knowledge (Marler, 1957, 1959). Thus the song of the Blue Tit, which throughout most of its European range has to co-exist with four or five other members of the genus, in Britain at least is fairly stereotyped and provides a good specific character. But on Tenerife, where it is the only tit species, it has a confusing variety of utterances. It is as if, with specific distinctiveness no longer required, individual distinctiveness has become valuable or at least allowable. Marler and Boatman (1951) found a rather similar situation in regard to the Goldcrest.

With the Chaffinch, perhaps because on the Continent it competes with no nearly related form but yet has, on the whole, a denser population, individual variation is advantageous provided it does not go beyond certain bounds. Hence the songs

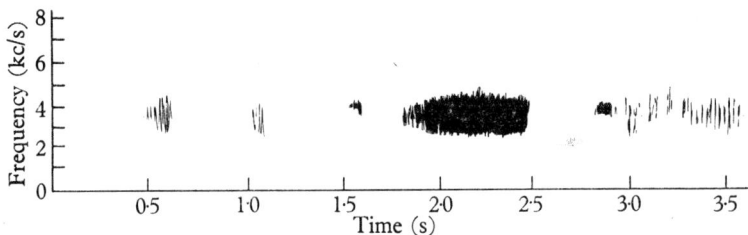

Fig. 56. Song of Brambling, recorded in Sweden. (Thorpe, 1958a.)

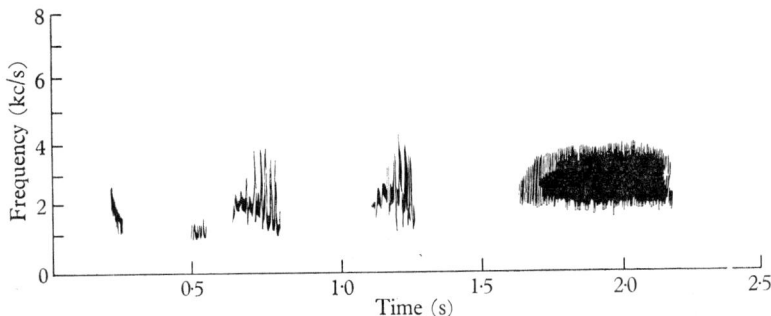

Fig. 57. Song of Brambling, recorded in aviary, Cambridge. (Thorpe, 1958a.)

of *coelebs* and *gengleri* are both specifically (but not subspecifically) and individually recognisable. The island subspecies, however, seem—at least from my own experience of *maderensis* in the Madeiran laurel forest (experience which is I think corroborated by the observations of others on other Atlantic islands)—to exist at a much lower population density. As a result, the Madeiran Chaffinches seem no longer to require the learned elaboration which is such a feature of European Chaffinches; their songs seem accordingly to have reverted, by the reduction or restriction of learning ability, in the direction of that simpler form which is nearer to the innate basis of the specific song.

The nearest relative of the Chaffinch on the European continent is the Brambling, *Fringilla montifringilla* (see Mayr, Andrew and Hinde, 1956). Its song (figs. 56 and 57) bears extremely little resemblance to that of the Chaffinch and provides a good instance of the unreliability of song as a generic character. The full song seems to consist of four or five notes with a fundamental from 1–4 kc. The extra phrase on the end of the song shown in fig. 56 is perhaps more correctly regarded as part of the subsong and not as belonging to the full song at all. This conclusion is perhaps supported by the song of the hybrid brambling × chaffinch described on p. 87 of the previous chapter.

From what has been said it is hard to avoid the conclusion that song differences must also on occasion play an important part in initiating as well as maintaining evolutionary divergences. It is of course hardly possible to obtain any conclusive evidence for this, but Dilger (1956) and Stein (1956) provide some evidence from play-back experiments with *Hylocichla* spp. that song differences are important in keeping populations apart.

CHAPTER 7

Sound-production and Hearing

THE fact that the vocal apparatus of birds consists not of the larynx and associated structures as in ourselves and the mammals generally, but of the syrinx, was one of the earliest known facts of avian internal anatomy. Roughly speaking, the syrinx is a bony chamber situated at the lower end of the trachea at

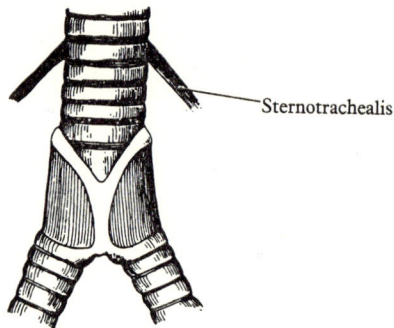

Fig. 58. Tracheo-bronchial syrinx of *Neotrepannis corruscans* (family Philepittidae). A simple type of syrinx. (Amadon, 1951.)

the junction of the two bronchi. This position, leaving as it does a relatively long resonating box between the syrinx and larynx, can plausibly be regarded as an adaptation allowing the production of notes far lower in tone than would otherwise be possible in such small animals.

In some groups of birds the syrinx consists simply of a modification of the first few bronchial rings, and in a few other groups it is constructed solely from the trachea itself. However, in all the birds dealt with in this book the syrinx contains both tracheal and bronchial components and so has been called a tracheo-bronchial syrinx. Figs. 58 and 59 show two examples of syringeal structure, the first taken from the family Philepittidae and the second from the sun-birds (Nectariniidae), and illustrate, respectively, a relatively simple, and a relatively complex type.

The syrinx of birds is characterised by having both extrinsic and intrinsic muscles. The extrinsic muscles are those such as the tracheo-clavicular and sterno-tracheal muscles which connect the vocal apparatus with other parts of the bird's anatomy. The intrinsic muscles are those which control the positions and tensions in the apparatus itself. Where, as in some of the ratite birds, and (as a result of secondary loss) in some of the Gallinae, there are no intrinsic muscles proper, the possibility of controlling the vocalisations must be extremely small. In the Herring Gull there is only one pair of intrinsic muscles (Rüppell, 1933) and consequently there will be only a slight possibility of directly controlling the vibration in the tympanic membranes

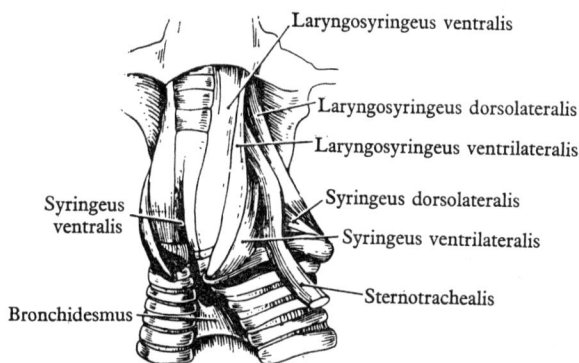

Fig. 59. Tracheo-bronchial syrinx of the sun bird (Nectariniidae) *Arachnothera longirostris*. (Koditz, 1925.) An example of a relatively complex type of syrinx.

which are, as we shall see, the prime source of sound production. Nevertheless, there are many anomalies: some birds which have a very simple syringeal musculature manage to produce surprisingly complex sounds, and others which have a most elaborate musculature produce little in the way of song. However, the groups which contain the best songsters are certainly those in which the syrinx has the most complex musculature. Another puzzle is provided by the fact that among many of the ducks and also other groups of birds which need not be mentioned here, a great many remarkable modifications of syringeal structure have been described, but in no case does there appear to be any clear correlation between the tracheal structure and the type or variety of sounds produced (Pyecraft, 1910). It must be remembered also that many groups of birds, particularly the ducks, have associated with this syrinx an asymmetrical and often large resonating-chamber or osseus bulla. Because of its rigid bony walls, this can hardly be a mechanism for modulation. As Pyecraft points out, if some of these structures in ducks are for modifying the voice then it is curious, to say the least, that in many ducks the female, which has no resonator, has the louder voice, and that ducks with precisely similar resonators have entirely different calls. Puzzles such as these, and they are many, suggest that perhaps a better understanding may be achieved by looking first at sound-producing structures which are already fairly well understood, such as the human vocal apparatus and some of our musical instruments, and that consideration of these may help us to isolate the various fundamental problems involved and guide us in interpreting some of the puzzling structures that we see in birds.

Helmholtz (1821–94) carried out his fundamental studies on the production of sounds very nearly a hundred years ago (1862). This work was the basis for understanding the mode of action of the human vocal-organs; but there is still a great deal to be learnt about our own methods of song and of speech. It is consequently not to be wondered at that when we come to consider the vocal-organs of birds we find that knowledge and understanding is negligible compared to that which we have for the human species. However, the information gained from new techniques of sound analysis not only throws a flood of light upon the mode of action of the human vocal apparatus, but also to some extent provides a short-cut towards the understanding of sound-production in birds, giving us at least a few clues as to how some of the structures we at present understand so imperfectly may be operating, and offering a number of suggestions for future investigation.

In man, of course, there is a vibratory apparatus which consists of the vocal-cords. The changing tensions exerted on these cords by the associated muscles results in modulation of the voiced sounds as the air passes over them. The human voice is further modulated by tongue and lips and—in properly controlled speech and song—by appropriate changes in the shape and dimensions of resonating-chambers which, in the human case, are the pharyngeal, oral and nasal cavities. Thus, when we speak or sing, our vocal-cords determine the pitch of the voice note, and the resonating system is made to conform, producing or suppressing some overtones and amplifying and emphasising others. Our ability to make our resonating-cavities conform in this way is, as Mackworth-Young (1953) points out, due on the one hand to the vigorous and precisely controlled action of the vocal-cords, and on the other to the fact that the throat cavity in which our vocal-cords are placed is easily variable in shape and has an elastic yielding wall. Mackworth-Young says 'If our throats were plain tubes of metal or hard wood their resonating tones would be so rigid and so strongly defined that the vocal-cords would be unable to maintain any other frequencies against them. As things are, the resonances of the throat-cavity, though adequate for reinforcing the vocal note, are not sufficiently strong or inflexible to oust the cords from their control of the pitch. Accordingly, the throat cavity and, with it, the mouth cavity also, are content to let the vocal-cords dictate the prime tone and to modulate their own resonances so as to reinforce such partials of the tone as lie within their respective compasses.' He then points out that the movements which effect this modulation are principally those of the tongue, lips and jaw and that these produce their effect by altering the size and shape of the cavities or of their openings, or both, thus producing resonances of different pitch.

When we come to compare wind instruments with the human voice, we see that most of them are constructed with finger-holes, valves, stops or other devices such that the effective resonating length of the tube can be changed and different fundamental tones achieved. The sounds produced by the passage of air through the instrument will, therefore, be primarily due to the limitations imposed by the rigid walls of the instrument. In instruments having a vibrator in the form of a reed, this is of course passive and the unyielding action of the resonating tube forces the reed (or, in the case of the trumpet, the vibrating lips of the player) to conform.

It is obvious that most song birds produce sounds which remind us more of wind instruments such as the flute, oboe and clarinet than of the human voice. How far, then, can the avian vocal apparatus in fact be operating after the manner of a wind instrument? A section through a characteristic bird syrinx, whether it be quite unspecialised as in the domestic fowl, with perhaps only a single pair of intrinsic muscles, or whether, as in the Blackbird, it is highly efficient for song and equipped with seven pairs of such muscles, reveals a structure which in essentials appears extraordinarily uniform through the bird world (fig. 60). There is a semi-lunar membrane attached to a bony rod, the pessulus, stretched across the chamber at the point where the two bronchi unite. This membrane, while it must obviously be set in motion by the passage of air, does not appear in most birds to have the direct muscular attachments

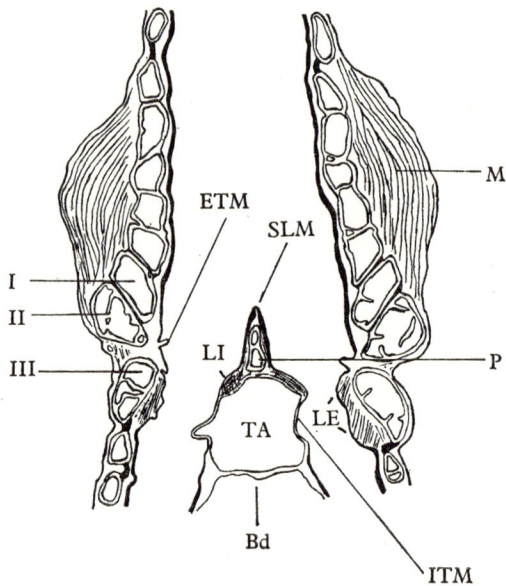

Fig. 60. Syrinx of a male Blackbird in longitudinal section to illustrate the typical structure. Bd = bronchidesmus membrane; ETM, ITM = exterior and interior tympanic membrane; LE and LI = external and internal lips; M = tracheo-bronchialis muscles; P = pessulus; SLM = semi-lunar membrane; TA = extension of anterior thoracic air sac; I, II and II bronchial semi-rings. (Thorpe, 1959, modified from Haecker.)

which would be needful if we are to suppose it to be acting as a vibrator in the same dominating manner as do the human vocal-cords. Besides this membrane there are, however, two other pairs of membranes, the internal and external tympaniform membranes. These may not only have muscles attached to them but are also situated so that muscles which control the move-ments of the adjacent tracheal semi-rings will indirectly be effective in controlling the tensions in them. It follows then that the passage of air up the bronchi through the syrinx into the trachea could, theoretically, set these membranes in vibratory motion and that the frequency of their vibration would naturally be controlled by the tension exerted on them by the adjacent muscles. Rüppell (1933) made a particular study of the vocal apparatus of the Herring Gull, comparing it with the domestic fowl and also species of crane (*Grus*), goose (*Anser*) and swan (*Cygnus*). The typical condition in such birds is for there to be two pairs of muscles, the broncho-tracheales and sterno-tracheales, only. The former (the intrinsic) pair would, it seems, give a slight possibility, but no more, of controlling the tensions in the tympanic membrane. Of course where there are no intrinsic muscles, as in the domestic fowl (where apparently they have been lost in recent evolution), there does not seem to be any possibility of direct control of these membranes. Such direct modulation as can be brought about in such forms would seem, then, to be the result of the action of the bronchotrachealis in affecting the form and dimensions of the resonating tube, the trachea. And although the vibrating membranes may be affected by the pressures in the air sacs and by the tensions in the adjacent tissues, it would seem that they must be very largely passive and subservient to the resonance of the tube. This seems to be the general picture in the more primitive birds and there are, therefore, good reasons for making a functional comparison between the vocal structures of these birds at least and some types of wind instrument.

Let us now compare the action of the vocal apparatus in bird and man. Since in mammals the voice is, of course, produced during exhalation (which is the passive part of respiration), it had been assumed that the vibrations of the semi-lunar membrane in birds were the prime cause of vocalisation and that the sound must be produced while the air is entering the bird's lung—which is the passive phase in bird respiration, corresponding vocally to our exhalation. The experiments of Miskimen (1951) suggested, however, that in the song birds the sound is produced during the active or exhalant phase of respiration,[1]

---

[1] I am indebted to Sir Gavin de Beer for an account of a canary belonging to Lieut.-Col. Anthony Taaffe which had suffered an accidental fistula of one of its main air sacs. The attempts of this bird to sing merely resulted in expulsion of air through the fistula, giving graphic demonstration that the song occurs during the active or exhalant phase of respiration.

and the semi-lunar membrane seems to have little or no function in the production of sound, which in fact originates in the vibrations set up in the tympanic membranes by the passage over them of air from the lungs. While, however, this picture seems plausible, the conclusion that the semi-lunar membrane is completely functionless is at least doubtful; nor does there seem to be any sound basis for the assumption of some earlier workers that if the semi-lunar membrane is to be activated, it must be by an inward passage of air. However, leaving this problem out of account for the moment, we have at any rate a clear picture of two pairs of membranes, the tensions in which can obviously be modified by special groups of muscles. Moreover, there is ample muscular equipment for modifying the shape, resistance and dimensions of the trachea or windpipe so that there is at least one resonator which can be actively modulated to conform with the vibrations of the tympanic membrane. So it looks as if the structure both of the human vocal apparatus and of a typical wind instrument may be fruitful in providing suggestive analogies in the study of avian vocal-organs.

One of the striking features which has emerged from the sound spectrographic study of bird vocalisations is the evidence that it has provided for a double or multiple sound-producing mechanism. Thus Potter, Kopp and Green (1947) reproduce a sound spectrogram of the song of a Brown Thrasher in which, at certain points in the song, it is quite clear that two notes in which no harmonic relationship can be seen, are being sounded at the same time. Analysis of the song of the Reed Warbler provides evidence for a similar effect, and Borror and Reese (1956) have shown with the Wood Thrush, one of the most beautiful songsters, that there is some overlapping of notes, with one note beginning before the preceding note ends, thus resulting in the bird uttering two or more independent songs at the same moment. In one song which they have recorded there is a period of about 0·1 s in length when no less than four separate notes are apparently being uttered simultaneously. A very striking case of this has recently been revealed by Dr Fae Hall's analysis (pers. comm.) of the long bouts of singing with which the male Gouldian Finch accompanies its dancing sexual display (fig. 61). Here there seem to be three different vocal mechanisms in simultaneous operation, one producing a somewhat drone-like 'continuo' while the other two produce an elaborate chirruping song above it. It thus appears that there must be, in some birds at least, more than one vibrator at work and, if the record of Borror and Reese is substantiated, there might conceivably be four! As will be evident from what has been said above, these could be the two sets of tympaniform membranes and, thirdly perhaps, the semi-lunar membrane. The fourth modulating mechanism, if indeed it really exists, is much more questionable. Schufeldt (1890) described in the Raven two pairs of muscles, the *constrictor glottidis* and the *thyreo-arytenoideus* which close and open respectively the structure in the superior larynx known as the *rima glottidis*. This structure has long been

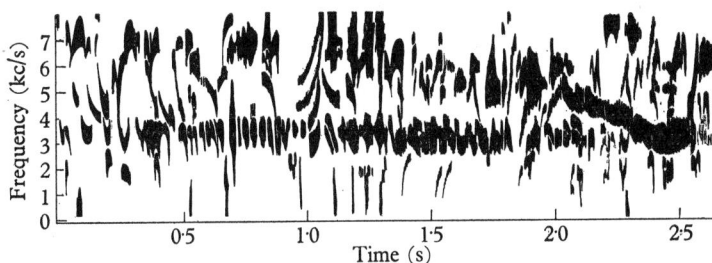

Fig. 61. Section of song of Gouldian Finch. There appear to be three different vocal mechanisms operating simultaneously, one producing a drone-like continuo, the other two an elaborate chirruping song above it. (From material supplied by F. Hall.)

known and Owen (1866), for various reasons which need not be gone into here, had assumed that this region—the superior larynx—functions after the manner of what we now call a 'start-stop modulator' for the voice, and that it was unable to perform any other functions. That he was correct in the first point seems undoubted; whether he was correct in the second is much more questionable. Thomson (1923) obviously considers that membranes on either side of the glottis can in some species be functioning as vibrators. If this is so, there is then no insuperable difficulty in seeing how the multiple notes of some birds can be produced. The structures we can find in the syrinx, the trachea and the larynx together appear to be sufficiently complex to be responsible, at least theoretically, for all the varied sounds which we find in the normal songs of birds.

However, the vocal performances of those birds which can imitate the human voice pose problems of quite a different order (Thorpe, 1959). Roughly speaking, there are two types of consonant-sound in human speech, the plosives (of which *p*, *b*, *t* and *d* are examples) and the fricatives (which include *f*, *v* and varieties of *s*, *z* and *ch* sounds, all on the whole of relatively high frequency). The first group, the plosives, really involve different ways of stopping and starting sounds more or less suddenly, with more or less explosive force, and with greater or less infusion of high frequencies. We accomplish this, of course, by using different parts of the mouth—lips, tongue and palate—and different combinations of these. Obviously, since birds can stop and start their sounds with extreme suddenness, we should expect them to produce something like our consonants; but since the tongue, larynx and mouth cavity are so different from ours, and since the overall size of the vocal-organs of most birds is so much smaller than ours, we should not expect sound spectrograms of birds' voices to show more than a slight and very general resemblance between the stopped sounds of birds and those which we ourselves produce. This is borne out by experimental evidence; thus the sound spectrogram of normal bird voices does not give us any very clear evidence of distinguishing between, say, *p* and *b* or *t* and *d*. Of course when we interpret bird sounds in human words, we include the characteristic consonants and vowels which make up those words, but the consonants we include may have little or nothing corresponding to them in the actual voice of the bird. We think *Cuculus canorus* says *Cuckoo*, but are we in fact very sure that it does not say *guggoo* or even *puppoo*? When we come to the fricatives, we find that the resemblances are a good deal closer and we can distinguish in bird vocalisations sounds which are closely similar to a number of our own fricative consonants; it is for this reason that when we attempt to represent the sounds of small birds in words we find ourselves making such lavish use of the letters 'f', 'v', 's', 'x' and 'z'. The characteristic 'high front' sounds (figs. 26 and 27) of birds, already referred to, contain a big range of frequencies, such as we normally associate with fricatives, coupled with an extremely efficient mechanism for start-stop modulation. If the sounds are of very short duration, that is, from 1 to 20 ms, we hear them as clicks, without any very definite pitch, although there is evidence that the birds themselves can analyse the pitch of such brief sounds more successfully than we can. To summarise, we seldom find any very close similarities between human consonants and the sounds made by birds as part of their normal repertoire, except those which depend on the range and relative intensity of the higher frequencies present.

The question of the bird production of vowels, however, is of particular significance. Phoneticians recognise twenty-three different vowels or vowel-like sounds in human speech. These are the incidental result of the fact that we human beings have more than one main resonator. As Mackworth-Young points out, the vowels occur whenever the throat or mouth cavities are stirred into resonance simultaneously, whether the stimulus is due to vocal cords, as in speech and song (when the sound is said to be voiced), or whether it is merely due to the air stream passing through both cavities, as in whispering. 'The only necessary condition is that the mouth should be open. We cannot speak, sing, whisper or even pant without uttering a vowel.' There are four types of modulation which occur in speech: (1) start-stop, (2) vocal-cord, (3) frictional, and (4) cavity modulation. (1) and (3) affect the flow of air from our lungs; (2) and (3) convert the flow into audible sound waves; and (4), broadly speaking, varies the quality of the sound. The different types of consonants we have been talking about are produced by differing combinations of these types of modulation, but always contain (1) or (3) or both. When pure vowels or vowel-like sounds are produced in ordinary speech, only (2) and (4) occur. Summarising briefly the result of recent study (Thorpe, 1959) one may say that in producing vowels the coupled cavities of mouth, nose and throat act in co-operation on the overtones produced by the vocal cords (and to some extent by frictional modulation) and, by suppressing some, give an apparent reinforcement that we recognise as the vocal resonance. These vocal resonances in the vowels are determined by the shapes and sizes of the resonators and are under very precise control by the movements of the lips, jaw, tongue and soft palate; but it stands to reason that this cavity modulation will affect the sounds produced by the vocal cords very much more than those produced by frictional modulation since the sounds produced by the vocal cords arise behind the cavities concerned, whereas those produced frictionally arise in front.

The characteristics of vowels as an expression of the resonances of these three main cavities are well illustrated by sound spectrograms. Fig. 62 shows the kind of patterns produced when the six main vowels are sounded. It will be seen that there are characteristic resonance bars which correspond to the frequencies at which the vocal resonances occur. There are actually four of these, numbered from below up, but the fourth may be very faint or imperceptible. The patterns of the vowels and vowel-like sounds are characterised by different combinations of bars. Of the resonance bars most frequently present in the vowel patterns, the second bar is the most important one, and this is known as the 'hub'. Bar one, the lowest, is limited in movement to a small interval at the bottom of the pattern, while bar three is both limited in its movement, and often weak, and sometimes absent. Bar two, however, derives its signifi-

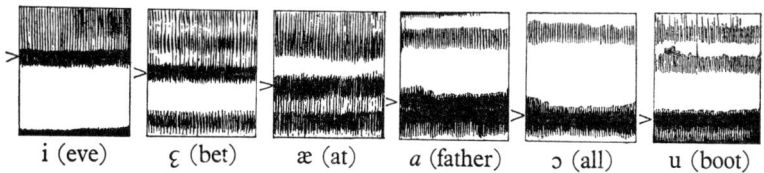

| i (eve) | ɛ (bet) | æ (at) | a (father) | ɔ (all) | u (boot) |

Fig. 62. Patterns of resonance in human speech, of the three main cavities produced when the six main vowels are sounded. The hub of the vowel (formant 2) is indicated in each case. (Thorpe, 1959, after Potter, Kopp and Green, 1947.)

cance from its relationship with one and three. The hub is thus the position of bar two, and can be defined as 'the visible or hidden position of bar two when the vowel is sounded alone' (Potter, Kopp and Green). Similarly, as we have said, consonants have potential vocal resonances which may or may not produce visible bars in their pattern. (They are much less in evidence in sound spectrograms because, as we have seen, the modulators producing the consonants are in front of the resonating cavities; but a human consonant may have a hub which is defined in just the same way—as the hidden position of bar two.) When we compare the six vowels, each of which has a different hub, we can see why—since the vertical scale is one of frequency—a succession of vowels can give us an impression of a series of sounds changing pitch. This brings us back, then, to the question: What, if anything, in the way of vowels can a talking-bird produce? At first sight, the vocal equipment does not appear to have the cavities necessary to enable birds to produce anything at all similar to our vowels. True, we often think and speak as if we believe birds to be uttering vowels. We might add the Wood Pigeon and Curlew to the Cuckoo already mentioned, and there is a common impression that the Yellow Bunting says 'A little bit of bread and no cheese', but we hardly need the sound spectrograph to tell us that the Yellow Bunting really says nothing of the kind. Such little phrases serve to remind us of particular bird-songs because the rhythm is appropriate and because the vowels that we include reflect approximately the same changes in the main hub that are found in bird-song. But although there are many early records alleging that Robins and other song birds can learn to talk (Lack, 1943), none of the sound spectrograms of any of the ordinary song birds that I had myself hitherto investigated or seen described gave any indication that birds can produce anything resembling the human vowel.[1]

This conclusion raises the problem of talking-birds. Surely parrots and budgerigars at least produce something like our vowels? However, such records as I was able to examine gave little support to any such conclusion, and for a long time I was inclined to believe that when a bird imitated the vowels of human speech, all that it did was to produce the right pitch changes, so giving the impression that a good imitation of human words had been effected. Subsequently, however (Thorpe, 1959), I have had to revise this opinion as a result of hearing and having access to recordings of an Indian Hill Mynah. The sound spectrograms shown in fig. 63 indicate that whatever may be lacking in the vocalisation of other talking-birds, this species at least can produce four perfectly genuine vowels, and probably many more. There is clear evidence of three and sometimes four vocal resonances, and that some at least of these (nos. 2 and 3) are under precise control.

Comparison with the performance of the talking-machine known as the Parametric Artificial Talking Device, suggests that whereas the very best of talking-birds, such as the Indian Hill Mynah, have a full equipment of resonators which can be modulated to form true vowel-sounds indistinguishable from those of human-beings, the inferior ones lack control of the third and probably also of the fourth (Thorpe, 1959). The

[1] Since writing this, I have obtained good recorded evidence that canaries can achieve very creditable imitations of human speech.

anatomical account of the bird vocal apparatus is not at present sufficiently precise to enable us to do more than guess at the cavities which could be taking part in the vowel sound production in these extraordinary imitating birds. It seems reasonable at first sight to suppose that the trachea plus the syrinx is the main cavity concerned, although when we consider that the trachea is particularly well designed for modification in shape and length to be effected (Rüppell, 1933), it may be that this is primarily responsible for the second formant of the vowel. Assuming that there are one or two resonating cavities below

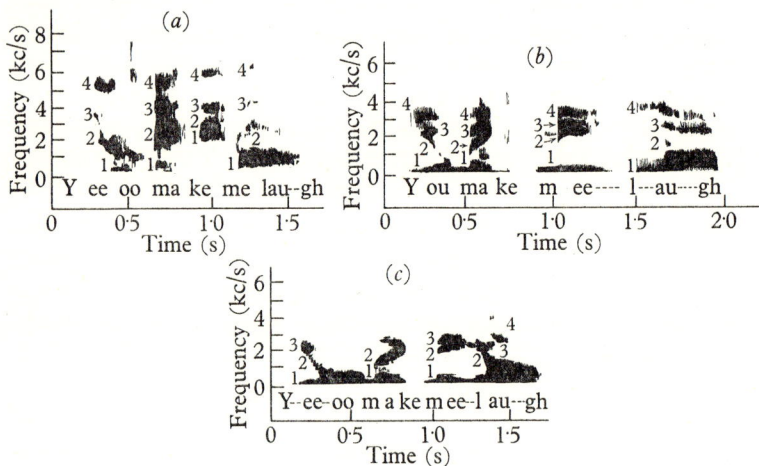

Fig. 63. The phrase 'You make me laugh' spoken by (a) Indian Hill Mynah; (b) adult human male, New Jersey accent; (c) adult human female, New England accent. (Thorpe, 1959.)

the superior larynx, it is hard to avoid the conclusion that the superior larynx itself acts as another in many species; and quite possibly—especially in the parrots, with their highly developed tongues—the mouth, with or without the nasal cavities, as another. A great deal more anatomical and physiological research will be necessary before we begin to have the answers to many of these questions. Nevertheless, there seems little doubt that within the order Aves we can find many birds with vocal organs functioning primarily after the manner of a wind instrument, having a resonating-chamber with rigid walls, and many others whose vocal apparatus works—in some respects at least—after the manner of the human voice, where the vocal cords dictate and modulate the fundamental and the cavities conform.

Quite apart from the physiological problems we have just been discussing in connection with bird imitations of human speech, the phenomena raise other questions as to evolution and biological function, the answers to which can as yet only be guessed. Talking-birds are so familiar to us that the significance of the performance has tended to be overlooked by ornithologists. No satisfactory evidence is available that either parrots or mynah birds ever use their remarkable powers of imitation in the wild; these seem to lie completely latent. How remarkable it is that the birds should be so much better than the primates in this respect. Within the primates a great variety of vocal mechanisms is to be found (Kelemen, 1958), yet the chimpanzee, which has by far the most complex and efficient vocal organs and which can produce a rich variety of sounds—even a sort of language—cannot be taught to imitate human speech. As Kelemen says, 'even this ape with possibly the highest development of mental qualities among animals, will be incapable, as has been demonstrated again and again, of imitating human speech since its own apparatus forms the basis of entirely different phonetic elements'. That the birds should have the anatomical and physiological equipment to enable them to overcome almost perfectly the problems of phonation posed by human speech seems, with our present knowledge, to be little short of miraculous.

Why these birds should learn to imitate human speech when kept in captivity is perhaps a little more understandable. Mowrer (1950) has suggested that the reason why parrots and Budgerigars learn to talk is that when kept in captivity, in close contact with human beings but away from their own kind, they develop a social attachment to their human keepers. They soon learn that vocalisations on their part tend to retain and increase the attention which they get from their owners, and as a result vocal production and, particularly, good vocal imitation is quickly reinforced by social contact. This seems to offer an explanation of the very well-known fact that, when learning, a parrot will tend to talk more when its owner is out of the room, or just after he has gone out, than when he is present. It is suggested that the bird is talking in an attempt to bring him back. This explanation seems plausible and is to a certain extent borne out by my own results. It is certainly true that in teaching Chaffinches new song-types, a live Chaffinch singing is a better model for inducing response in the experimental bird than a tape-recorder, however frequently the latter repeats the song to be learned. There may, of course, be a number of explanations of this, but it seems likely that it is because the live bird 'answers back', whereas a tape-machine merely goes off at pre-determined intervals, irrespective of the response of the hearer. If Mowrer is right about the psychology of talking-birds, it appears very similar to the human infant's first steps in learning to talk. Birds and babies, according to this hypo-thesis, both make their first efforts at reproducing words or other sounds because these sounds seem good to them—they are in fact self-stimulatory. Mothers often talk or croon to their children when attending to them, and so the sound of the mother's voice has often become associated with comfort-giving measures. So it is to be expected that when the child, alone and uncomfortable, hears his own voice, this will likewise have a consoling, comforting effect. To quote Mowrer, 'in this way it may be supposed that the infant will be rewarded for his own first babbling and jabbering without any necessary reference to the effects they produce on others'. Before long, however, he will learn that if he succeeds in making the kind of sound his mother makes, he will get more interest, affection and attention in return; so the stage is set for the learning of human language. In spite of all the differences, it seems hard not to believe that something of the same sort is happening in the learning of human speech by pet birds.

It is everywhere agreed that frequency-analysis or harmonic-analysis is the essential basis of 'hearing' in at least the higher vertebrates—that is to say, the fish, birds and mammals—as against hearing by the analysis of amplitude-modulation which predominates in the insects. The existence, in the ear of the mammals, of an elaborate organ of Corti and its associated basilar membrane and inner and external hair cells which are in contact with the terminal fibres of the acoustic nerve and are thus the ultimate sensory cells of the organ of hearing, had long provided what seemed to be almost overwhelming circum-stantial evidence for Helmholtz's resonance theory of hearing. This postulates that different portions of the basilar membrane vibrate selectively in response to different frequencies—that is to say, the process of frequency-analysis takes place in the inner ear and the results of this frequency-analysis are transmitted, without substantial further change, via the auditory nerve to the brain. But over many decades now an increasing number of difficulties for this 'classical' theory, in its various forms, have appeared and the opinion now widely held is that even in mammals with the most highly developed ears only a relatively small part of the process of sound analysis actually takes place in the sense organ itself, and that the lower and some of the middle tones are transferred directly to the brain—the so-called volley principle—and are subject to analysis there. The fundamental principles of the action of the vertebrate ear are far too complex and controversial to be discussed here. Readers who wish for fuller information on the subject are referred to the works of Wever (1949), Stevens and Davis (1938), Galambos (1954) and Pumphrey (1961).

In birds the cochlea with its associated basilar membrane and organ of Corti shows rather uniform features throughout the whole class. Schwartzkopff (1955a) has shown that the size of both the drum membrane and the cochlea increases relatively, not absolutely, with increasing body size. It follows that the auditory organs of many small birds (which, of course, includes many good songsters and consequently, one would suppose, many species which have good auditory capabilities) remain smaller than those of large-sized representatives of the same or other systematic groups. This suggests that the bird ear is not performing the sound analysis by means of spatial separation of sensory elements excited by different tones. Schwartzkopff (1955b) also suggests that the compact design of the sensory cells and the fact that they remain joined to the tectorial membrane for life, also constitutes an argument against peripheral sound analysis; moreover, the roof of the canal containing the sensory cells, the *ductus cochlearis*, has become in birds the heavy *tegmentum vasculosum*, rich in unicellular glands and small blood vessels, which—Schwartzkopff concludes—will damp any resonating vibrations of the inner ear liquor. Finally, although we have no precise evidence as to the hearing range of any of the parrots, their ability to imitate idiosyncrasies of tone of the human voice shows that they must have remarkably good powers of frequency discrimination. Yet there is no evidence that the length of the basilar membrane or of the cochlea itself is either relatively or absolutely high when compared with that of a large number of other species of birds (Schwartzkopff, 1955a and 1957). Fig. 64 shows the immense difference in length between the basilar membrane of man and parrot.

Although all these facts have been cited as evidence that frequency-analysis in birds takes place not in the hearing organ but in the brain, there is much to be said on the other side. Thus Pumphrey (1948, 1961) suggests that the greater number of hair cells per unit length of basilar membrane in the avian ear indicates a greater power of intensity discrimination compared with mammals and that this removes many of the diffi-

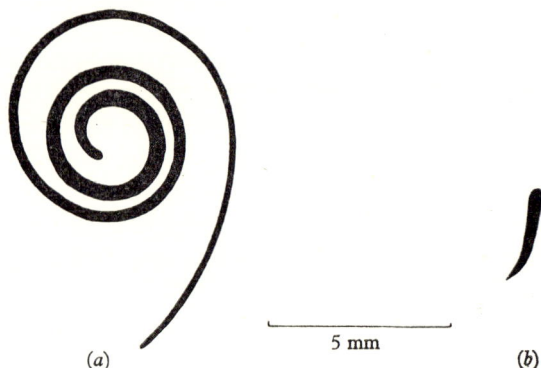

(a)   5 mm   (b)

Fig. 64. Diagram showing the relative size of the basilar membrane of man (a) and a parrot, *Chrysotis amazonica* (b), with equally good hearing. From Schwartzkopff (1955a) after Wever (1949) and Denker (1907).

culties in the way of the classical theory. Thus if the avian cochlea is in fact ten times as sensitive to changes in amplitude as is the mammalian it is theoretically possible for the same degree of frequency discrimination over a given band of frequencies to be achieved with one tenth the number of frequency-sensitive elements; and each element need be only one tenth as selective and consequently may respond *ten times as fast*. So the avian cochlea gains over the mammalian in simplicity, ruggedness and speed, and perhaps pays for it not by loss in powers of frequency discrimination, but by a tenfold decrease in signal/noise ratio. This is equivalent to saying that the absolute threshold theoretically attainable by the bird's cochlea is 10 db higher than in the mammal. This, however,

TABLE 2. *The hearing range of various birds compared with that of man*

Species	Lower limit (c/s)	Greatest sensitivity (c/s)	Upper limit (c/s)	Method	Author
Homo sapiens	16	1,000–2,800	10,000–24,000	—	—
Melopsittacus undulatus	40	2,000	14,000	D	Knecht (1940)
Loxia curvirostra	—	—	20,000	D	Knecht (1940)
Sturnus vulgaris	< 100	2,000	15,000	D	Granit (1941)
Passer domesticus	—	—	18,000	D	Granit (1941)
Erithacus rubecula	—	—	21,000	D	Granit (1941)
Chloris chloris	—	—	20,000	D	Granit (1941)
Pyrrhula pyrrhula	< 100	3,200	—	D	Schwartzkopff (1949)
	< 200	3,200	20,000–25,000	C	Schwartzkopff (1952)
Fringilla coelebs	< 200	3,200	29,000	C	Schwartzkopff (1955a)
Pica pica	< 100	800–1,600	21,000	C	Schwartzkopff (1955a)
Corvus brachyrhynchos	< 300	1,000–2,000	> 8,000	D	Trainer (1946)
Falco sparverius	300	2,000	> 10,000	D	Trainer (1946)
Anas platyrhynchos	300	2,000–3,000	> 8,000	D	Trainer (1946)
Columba livia	300	1,000–2,000	—	D	Trainer (1946)
			12,000	D	Wassiljew (1933)
	50	1,800–2,400	11,500	C	Wever and Bray (1936)
Asio otus	< 100	6,000	18,000	D	Schwartzkopff (1955a)
Strix aluco	< 100	3,000–6,000	21,000	C	Schwartzkopff (1955a)
Bubo bubo	60	1,000	> 8,000	D	Trainer (1946)

C = Conditioning method; D = cochlea-potential method. (From Schwartzkopff, 1955a.)

is so small as to be perhaps of little moment for, in a random population of young human adults all regarded as having normal powers of hearing, the individual differences in threshold greatly exceed 10 db.

It is natural to assume that birds can hear tones of the same range as those which they produce. However, this is by no means always the case; there are a number of exceptions. Table 2 shows how training methods reveal that the upper limit of hearing—provided the sounds are of normal intensity— is usually reached at about 20,000 cycles, but that when intensities of sound greater than those normally encountered are used experimentally cochlear potentials have been detected at 25,000 to 30,000 cycles. The notes of song birds no doubt sometimes contain still higher harmonics (Brand, 1938) but it does not follow that they are of any significance to the bird, nor is there any evidence that any high proportion of the sound energy is coming over at these levels. Schwartzkopff has provided evidence that the highest sensitivity of hearing of a given species which in song birds reaches the human threshold (and in owls probably exceeds it) is mostly found at the modal centre of the voice of that species. It is of course more or less inevitable that among related species the larger ones have lower voices

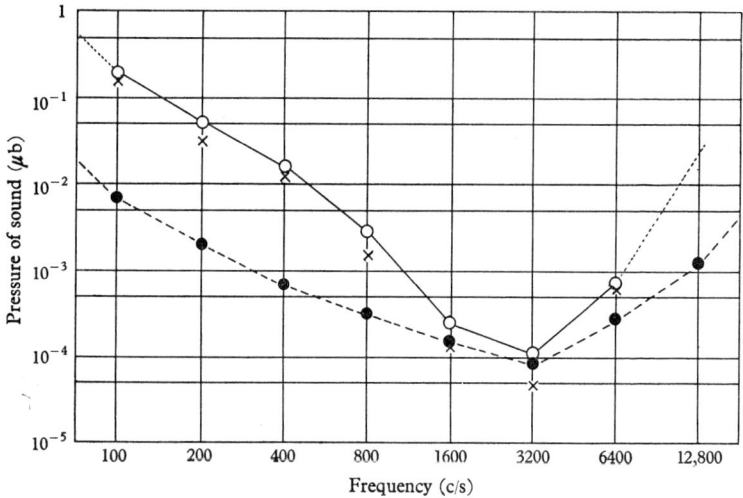

Fig. 65. Threshold of hearing of the Bullfinch (upper curve) and man (lower curve). × = best value for a single bird. (Schwartzkopff, 1949.)

and indeed it would be physically impossible for many small birds to make sounds as low as those uttered by crows, jays, magpies and owls. It is, however, very interesting that some owls are sensitive to tones above the mid-point of the voice of song birds; these presumably correspond to the squeak of mice. Collias and Joos (1953) have shown that baby chicks hear almost nothing but the low clucking of their mother (about 400 cycles) while the hen reacts with preference to the high cheeping (about 3000 cycles) of her young. Schwartzkopff suggests that there is probably selective value in chicks being able to hear only the mother and not their fellow chicks. Fig. 65 (Schwartzkopff, 1949) compares the sensitivity of the hearing-capacity of the Bullfinch and of man at different frequencies. It will be seen that in both the greatest sensitivity occurs at round about 3200 cycles and that over the whole range man is somewhat better than the Bullfinch, although at the peak the best bird studied showed a sensitivity higher than that of the mean for man.

Another very important aspect of hearing concerns the power of temporal resolution or, as it has been called, the time-perception smear. This is an indication of the number of separate successive sounds which can be heard as distinct within a given time-interval. Pumphrey (1961) cites evidence for thinking that a small bird does about ten times better than we do in this respect. Kaubmann (1950) shows how man's judgement of number begins to fail when required to count more than three short impulses of sound delivered at faster than 0·1 s apart. It is not easy to obtain unequivocal evidence of the bird's ability in this respect. There are certainly many examples amongst bird-song records of repetition of notes at a much smaller interval, and although this does not necessarily imply that the bird hears them as distinct there are reasons for assuming this to be so. Ansley (1954) demonstrated that slowed playback of a recording of the voice of the Whippoorwill (*Caprimulgus vociferus*) proves the song to have a five-note score, not three notes as the naked ear suggests, and that this five-note phrase is almost the same as that of the related Chuckwill's Widow (*C. carolinensis*) excepting for the fact that the song is delivered so fast that we usually hear but three of the five notes. These extra notes might, of course, be in the nature of transients and be neither under the control of, nor distinguishable by, the bird in question. However, Ansley points out that a record of the Mockingbird imitating a number of species, among them the Whippoorwill, gives exactly the same phenomenon as the record of the Whippoorwill itself. He assumes this to be good evidence that the mocking birds have a smaller time-perception smear than man. Recordings of a Phoebe, the Carolina Wren, the American Robin and the Wood Thrush support this general conclusion.

Pumphrey points out that it is a fundamental rule of physics that frequency analysis takes time. The more precise we wish the analysis of frequency to be, the longer must be the duration of the tone to enable it to be determined. Conversely, if an estimate of frequency has to be very quick because the note is of short duration, then the analysis can only be relatively coarse.

From this it must be concluded that the accuracy with which the frequency of a sound can be determined, by the sound spectrograph or any other method, is proportional to its duration. Applying this to bird-song, we notice that notes of extremely short duration will sound more or less click-like, whatever their frequency spectrum. They may be too short for the frequency to be determined properly by physical methods and they are certainly too short to give the human ear any impression of pitch. The only way out of the impasse is an improvement in the sensitivity of the device to amplitude changes.

The assumptions made about the bird's ear do not necessarily mean that it is less efficient than man's. If it is used for listening to sounds which are changing rapidly in frequency and intensity, an ear with a short time-constant can extract more information from the sound and nothing at all is lost by poor frequency-discrimination, provided that the nervous system can accept the information as fast as the ear can make it available—that is to say, that the time-constant of the nervous system is matched to that of the ear. The Oil Bird, *Steatornis caripensis*, uses a frequency of about one-tenth that used by bats for echo-location purposes. It therefore seems inevitable that the minimum size of object that it can detect must be greater than the minimum for bats in about the same ratio. It probably does not anyway want to detect flying insects, but even to locate and avoid the walls of the cave in rapid flight one must assume a very short time-constant of the ear as compared with the human ear. Griffin (1958) found that the frequency of the clicks emitted by the Oil Bird lies in most cases between 6000 and 10,000 c/s, with an average of about 7300. The pulses are extremely short, comparable to that of bat pulses (between 1 and 1·5 ms), and occasionally very short pulses of one or two waves will be found. Further studies will probably be necessary before one can completely exclude the possibility that high-frequency components are important to the bird under some conditions, but at present there is no definite reason for thinking so. The only other bird genus known to practice echo-location is *Collocalia* (the swiftlets of birds'-nest soup fame). Present information suggests that they are not dissimilar from the oil birds in regard to sound-production and hearing and in using these abilities for echo-location.

Knecht (1940) carried out extensive studies on bird hearing by means of the conditioning technique. His main subjects were Parrakeet and Crossbill, but he also extended his investigations to Linnet, Siskin, Goldfinch, Serin, Canary and Starling. His results as to hearing range have been included in Table 2 and need not be discussed again. In the middle part of the hearing range some birds were able to distinguish a difference of 2–5 c/s and with a 10-cycle interval the differentiating ability of the bird was as good as or better than that of man. Knecht found that the tone memory for small frequency differences was extraordinarily good; a 20-cycle difference can be remembered for hours, 5 cycles up to 1 h, 1–2 cycles up to 3 min in the best case. Coming to the upper registers, at the fourth octave the bird can hardly distinguish a quarter-tone, and at the sixth octave when given a diminished third or an augmented second, the bird's performance was similar to man or worse. Thus the interval d^6/e^6 which equals 1137 cycles, was retained up to 1 h, but at the fourth octave a 40-cycle interval could be equally well remembered. Training for simultaneous interval was also possible; thus at the third octave it was possible to train birds to distinguish between the third F and A as food tone and a fourth E and A as counter-tone after a considerable length of training. This differentiation is, of course, very easy for man, but was apparently more difficult for the bird. My own work on the Chaffinch (Thorpe, 1958a) showed that although this species normally maintains a remarkable constancy in the pitch of its song, it can—particularly in the subsong—transpose, and what is recognised is not a constant pitch but a temporal pattern of sound. Similar evidence is provided by Knecht and it seems likely to be the general rule. Finally, as we should expect, Knecht was unable to find any evidence that the European concepts of consonance and dissonance were applicable to birds. He had no evidence that sounds pleasant to the human ear were preferred to those which are unpleasant to us, as reinforcement of the conditioning situation. The present overall picture of the hearing abilities of birds which thus emerges suggests that it is similar to our own in general range and ability to discriminate pitch. Song birds and parrots certainly approach human abilities, although the performance of pigeons remains below that even of some fishes (Schwartzkopff, 1955b).

It is difficult to make any general statement about the ability of bird's ears for the localisation of sound. The hearing organs of insects are primarily displacement receptors, and since particle displacement is directional the organs will possess at least an inherent possibility of detecting direction. With birds and mammals, whose ears are pressure receptors, this possibility is absent, and the ability to localise the source of a sound must depend on three cues. First, the time of arrival of the sound at the two ears; second, the fact that the intensity is greater at the nearer ear since the head casts a sound shadow; and third, the rapid changes of pressure that constitute the sound will occur slightly earlier in the nearer ear—in other words, there will be a phase difference at the two ears. All three types of difference can be detected by man and it is a natural assumption that they can also be detected by other mammals with similar ears. It has been shown earlier in this book (p. 29) that many of the utterances of birds can be plausibly understood by considering them as adapted or not adapted, as the case may be, to provide these cues for localisation. In owls, which hunt their mouse prey primarily by hearing, Pumphrey and others have suggested that the asymmetry of the external ear will help by providing a parallax-fix in the vertical as well as the horizontal plane.

In conclusion we can say, with Galambos, that the capacity for dealing with tones, as measured by psychological testing, is not remarkably dissimilar for fish, birds and men. Yet, as he points out, the neural equipment of these is in many respects enormously different, and it is clear that neither a refined cochlea nor a highly developed auditory nervous system is a prerequisite for quite excellent tone discrimination. Mammals can distinguish tones as effectively as birds, and so the elaborate anatomical refinements that are so characteristic of the mammalian auditory apparatus seem irrelevant to the central problem. Again, as Galambos says, if we suppose that the structures with which man achieves his analysis of tone must also operate in fish, birds and cat, then we can at once play down the importance of, for example, the dorsal cochlear nucleus and superior olivary region (which are reduced in man in comparison to the cat), the cerebral cortex (which is absent in the bird), and the cochlea itself (which is absent in fishes). The question which cannot be answered at present is whether there is a common minimum neural equipment in all these forms that perceives and discriminates tones. In fact many of the most important questions raised by the comparative study of vertebrate hearing organs remain as yet unanswered.

REFERENCES

Amadon, D. (1951). Le pseudo-souimanga de Madagascar. *Rev. Hist. nat. appl. (Oiseaux)*, **21**, 59–63. [106]

Andrew, R. J. (1957*a*). The aggressive and courtship behaviour of certain Emberizinae. *Behaviour*, **10**, 255–308. [27, 34]

Andrew, R. J. (1957*b*). A comparative study of the calls of *Emberiza* spp. *Ibis*, **99**, 27–42. [19, 25, 27, 37]

Andrew, R. J. (1961). *Behaviour*. (In the Press.) [19, 28]

Angell, J. R. and Fite, W. (1901). The monaural localisation of sound. *Psychol. Rev.* **8**, 225–46. [62]

Ansley, H. (1954). Do birds hear their songs as we do? *Proc. Linn. Soc. N.Y.* Nos. 63–5, 39–40. [60, 125]

Armstrong, E. A. (1946). The coloration of sea-birds. *Birds of Britain*, no. 2, 15–19. [33]

Armstrong, E. A. (1947). *Bird Display and Behaviour*. London. [50]

Armstrong, E. A. (1955). *The Wren*. London. [35, 36, 37, 43, 48, 53, 98]

Barber, D. R. (1948). Chronometric observations of the song of *Fringilla coelebs* L. *Nature, Lond.*, **161**, 277. [44]

Barber, D. R. (1959). Singing pattern of the common chaffinch, *Fringilla coelebs*. *Nature, Lond.*, **183**, 129. [44]

Benson, C. W. (1948). Geographical voice variation in African birds. *Ibis*, **90**, 48–71. [99]

Bergman, G. (1946). Die Steinwälzer *Arenaria i. interpres* in seiner Beziehung zur Umwelt. *Acta zool. fenn.* **47**, 1–151. [26]

Bicknell, E. P. (1884–5). A study of the singing of our birds. *Auk*, **1**, 60–71, 126–40, 209–18, 322–32; **2**, 144–54, 249–62. [6]

Böker, H. (1923). Der Gesang der Vögel und der periodische Ablauf der Spermatogenese. Ein Beitrag zur biologischen Anatomie der Geschlechtsvorgänge. *J. Orn., Lpz.*, **71**, 169–96. [6]

Borror, D. J. (1956). Variation in Carolina wren songs. *Auk*, **73**, 211–29. [90, 100]

Borror, D. J. (1959). Variation in the songs of the rufous-sided thowee. *Wilson Bull.* **71**, 54–72. [100]

Borror, D. J. and Reese, C. R. (1956). Vocal gymnastics in wood thrush songs. *Ohio J. Sci.* **56**, 177–82. [112]

Borror, D. J. and Reese, C. R. (1959). Mocking bird imitations of Carolina wren. *Bull. Mass. Audubon Soc.* 16 pp. [89]

Brand, A. R. (1938). Vibration frequencies of passerine bird song. *Auk*, **55**, 263–8. [124]

Brown, P. E. and Davies, M. G. (1949). *Reed Warblers*. Foray Publications, East Molesey, Surrey. [43]

Bullough, W. S. (1942). The reproductive cycles of the British and Continental races of the starling. *Phil. Trans. Roy. Soc.* B, **231**, 165–246. [51]

Chapman, F. M. (1940). A post-glacial history of *Zonotrichia capensis*. *Bull. Amer. Mus. Nat. Hist.* **77**, 381–438. [99]

Cherry, C. (1957). *On Human Communication: A Review, a Survey and a Criticism.* New York and London. [7, 13]

Collias, N. E. (1960). An ecological and functional classification of animal sounds. In Lanyon and Tavolga, pp. 368–91. [30]

Collias, N. E. and Jahn, L. R. (1959). Social behaviour and breeding success in Canada Geese (*Branta canadensis*) confined in semi-natural conditions. *Auk*, **76**, 478–509. [25]

Collias, N. and Joos, M. (1953). The spectrographic analysis of the sound signals of the domestic fowl. *Behaviour*, **5**, 175–89. [17, 18, 20, 22, 37, 124]

Cox, P. R. (1944). A statistical investigation into bird song. *Brit. Birds*, **38**, 3–9. [53, 54]

Craig, W. (1943). The song of the wood pewee (*Myochanes virens*). *N.Y. State Mus. Bull.* **334**, 6–186. [5, 63]

Curio, E. (1959). Verhaltensstudien am Trauerschnäpper. Berlin. (Beiheft, 3, *Z. Tierpsychol.*) [35, 37, 54]

Damsté, P. H. (1947). Experimental modifications of the sexual cycle of the greenfinch. *J. Exp. Biol.* **24**, 20–35. [53]

Darwin, C. (1872). *Expression of the Emotions in Man and Animals.* London. [21]

Davis, J. (1958). Singing behaviour and the gonad cycle of the rufous-sided towhee. *Condor*, **60**, 308–36. [6, 41]

Delacour, J. (1943). A revision of the subfamily Estrildinae of the family Ploceidae. *Zoologica, N.Y.*, **28**, 69–86. [94]

Denker, A. (1907). *Das Höhrorgan und die Sprechwirkzeuge der Papagien.* Wiesbaden. [122]

Dilger, W. C. (1956). Hostile behaviour and reproductive isolating mechanisms in the avian genera *Catharus* and *Hylocichla*. *Auk*, **73**, 313–53. [105]

Falconer, D. S. (1941). Observations on the singing of the chaffinch. *Brit. Birds*, **35**, 98–104. [xii]

Fant, G. (1958). Modern instruments and methods for acoustic studies of speech. *Acta Polytechnica Scandinavica Physics including Nucleonics.* Series 1. [xi]

Fish, W. R. (1953). A method for the objective study of bird songs and its application to the analysis of Bewick wren songs. *Condor*, **55**, 250–7. [xi]

Frings, H., Frings, B., Cox, B. and Pissner, L. (1955). Auditory and visual mechanisms in food-finding behaviour of the herring gull. *Wilson Bull.* **67**, 155–70. [23, 37]

Galambos, R. (1954). The neural mechanisms of audition. *Physiol. Rev.* **34**, 495–528. [121, 128]

Garstang, W. (1922). *Songs of the Birds.* London. [13]

Goethe, F. (1954). Vergleichende Beobachtungen über das Verhalten der Silbermöwe (*Larus a. argentatus*) und der Geringsmöwe (*Larus f. fuscus*). *Proc. XI Int. Orn. Congr.* 577–82. [10]

Gooch, G. B. (1952). Variations in cirl bunting song during bathing. *Brit. Birds*, **45**, 407–8. [62]

Granit, O. (1941). Beiträge zur Kenntnis der Gehörsinns der Vogel. *Ornis fenn.* **18**, 49–71. [123]

Griffin, D. R. (1958). *Listening in the Dark.* New Haven. [126]

Haartmann, L. von (1956). Territory in the pied flycatcher, *Muscicapa hypoleuca. Ibis,* **98**, 460–75. [44]

Haecker, V. (1900). *Der Gesang der Vögel, seine anatomische und biologischen Grundlagen.* Jena. [6]

Haecker, V. (1916). Reizphysiologisches ü. Vogelzug und Frühgesang. *Biol. Zbl.* **36**, 403–31. [6]

Hall-Craggs, J. (1961). The development of song in the blackbird. (In the Press.) [62, 90, 91]

Hartshorne, C. (1956). The monotony threshold in singing birds. *Auk.* **73**, 176–92. [3]

Hartshorne, C. (1958). The relation of bird song to music. *Ibis,* **100**, 421–45. [3]

Herrick, E. H. and Harris, J. O. (1957). Singing female canaries. *Science,* **125**, 1299–300. [51]

Herzog, G. (1941). Do animals have music? *Bull. Amer. Musicological Soc.* no. 5, 3–4. [2]

Hinde, R. A. (1952). The behaviour of the great tit and some other related species. *Behaviour Suppl.* no. 2, 1–201. [16, 24, 25, 27, 37]

Hinde, R. A. (1958). Alternative motor patterns in chaffinch song. *Anim. Behav.* **6**, 211–18. [86]

Hoos, D. (1937). De Vinkenbaan. *Ardea,* **26**, 173–202. [53]

Howard, H. E. (1907). *The British Warblers: A History with Problems of their Lives.* London. [42]

Howard, H. E. (1920). *Territory in Bird Life.* London. [42]

Hüchtker, R. and Schwartzkopff, J. (1958). Soziale Verhaltensweisen bei hörenden und gehörlosen Dompfaffen (*Pyrrhula pyrrhula* L.). *Experientia,* **14**, 106–11. [26]

Ingraham, S. E. (1938). Instinctive music. *Auk,* **55**, 614–28. [xii]

Joos, M. (1948). Acoustic phonetics. *Language,* 24, no. 2 Suppl. (*Language Monogr.* no. 23, 1–136). [ix]

Kaubmann, R. E. (1950). Studies in judged number. *J. Genet. Psychol.* **43**, 167–94. [125]

Kelemen, G. (1958). Physiology of phonation in primates. *Logos,* **1**, 32–5. [119]

Kilham, L. (1959). Mutual tapping of the red-headed woodpecker. *Auk,* **76**, 235–6. [49]

Kiriline, L. de (1954). The voluble singer of the tree-tops. *Audubon (Annu.) Mag.* **56**, 109–11. [46, 55]

Klokaars, B. (1941). Studier över Fågelsångens dagsrhythmik. *Ornis fenn.* **18**, 73–110. [53]

Knecht, S. (1940). Über den Gehorsinn und die Musikalität der Vogel. *Z. vergl. Physiol.* **27**, 171–232. [126]

Koditz, W. (1925). Über die Syrinx einiger Clamatores und Ausländischer Oscines. *Z. vis. Zool.* **126**, 70–144. [107]

Koehler, O. (1951). Der Vogelsange als vorstuffe von musik und sprach. *J. Orn.* **93**, 3–20. [63]

Koehler, O. (1956). Thinking without words. *Proc. XIV Intern. Zool. Congr. Copenhagen*, pp. 75–88. [11]

Lack, D. (1943). *The Life of the Robin*. London. [15, 117]

Lack, D. and Southern, H. N. (1949). Birds of Tenerife. *Ibis*, **91**, 607–26. [103]

Lanyon, W. E. (1957). The comparative biology of the meadow larks, *Sturnella*, in Wisconsin. *Publications of the Nuttal Ornithological Club*, no. **1**, 1–67. Cambridge, Mass. [86, 99]

Lanyon, W. E. and Tavolga, W. N. (1960) (eds.). *Animal Sounds and Communication*. Washington, D.C. [10]

Lewis, L. B. and Dobb, L. V. (1948). A sexual transformation of the osseus bulla in duck embryos following administration of oestrogen. *Physiol. Zool.* **21**, 65–69. [52]

Linsdale, J. M. (1928). Variations in the fox sparrow (*Passerella iliaca*) with reference to natural history and osteology. *Univ. Calif. Publ. Zool.* **30**, 251–392. [100]

Lister, D. (1953 a). Secondary song: a tentative classification. *Brit. Birds*, **46**, 139–43. [65]

Lister, D. (1953 b). Secondary song of some Indian birds. *Bombay Nat. Hist. Soc.* **51**, 699–706. [70]

Mackworth-Young, G. (1953). *What happens in Singing*. London. [109]

Marler, P. (1952). Variations in the song of the chaffinch, *Fringilla coelebs*. *Ibis*, **94**, 458–72. [103]

Marler, P. (1955). Characteristics of some animal calls. *Nature, Lond.*, **176**, 6–7. [93]

Marler, P. (1956). The voice of the chaffinch and its function as language. *Ibis*, **98**, 231–61. [10, 25, 27, 28, 37, 43, 102]

Marler, P. (1957). Specific distinctiveness in the communication signals of birds. *Behaviour*, **11**, 13–29. [16, 33, 34, 94, 103]

Marler, P. (1959). Developments in the study of animal communication. Ch. 4 in *Darwin's Biological Work: Some Aspects Reconsidered*, ed. P. R. Bell. Cambridge. [30, 31, 33, 90, 93, 97, 98, 103]

Marler, P. (1960). Bird songs and mate selection. In Lanyon and Tavolga, pp. 348–67. [87, 93]

Marler, P. and Boatman, D. J. (1951). Observations on the birds of Pico, Azores. *Ibis*, **93**, 90–9. [100, 104]

Marler, P. and Isaac, D. (1960). Physical analysis of a simple bird song as exemplified by the chipping sparrow. *Condor*, **62**, 124–35. [x]

Marshall, A. J. (1950). The function of vocal mimicry in birds. *Emu*, **50**, 5–16. [89]

Marshall, A. J. (1960–61). *Biology and Comparative Anatomy of Birds*. London. [121, 122, 125]

Mayr, E. (1942). *Systematics and the Origin of Species*. New York. [99]

Mayr, E. (1956). Gesange und Systematik. *Beiträge zur Vogelkunde*. **5**, 112–17. [97, 100]

Mayr, E., Andrew, R. J. and Hinde, R. A. (1956). Die systematische Stellung der Gattung *Fringilla*. *J. Orn.* **97**, 258–73. [105]

Messmer, E. and Messmer, I. (1956). Die Entwicklung der Lautausserungen und einiger Verhaltensweisen der Amsel. *Z. Tierpsychol.* **13**, 341–441. [37, 90]

Metfessel, M. (1928). A photographic method of measuring pitch. *Science*, **68**, 430–32. [xii]

Metfessel, M. (1929). The strobophotograph. *J. Genet. Psychol.* **2**, 135–9. [xii]

Metfessel, M. (1934). Strobophotography in birds' singing. *Science*, **79**, 412–13. [xii]

Miller, L. (1952). Auditory recognition of predators. *Condor,* **54**, 89–92. [24]

Miller, W. J. and Miller, L. S. (1958). Synopsis of behaviour traits of the ring dove. *Anim. Behav.* **6**, 3–8. [37]

Miskimen, M. (1951). Sound production in passerine birds. *Auk*, **68**, 493–504. [111]

Montagu, G. (1802). *Ornithological Dictionary.* London. [45]

Mowrer, O. H. (1950). The psychology of talking birds: a contribution to language and personality theory. Ch. 24 of *Learning Theory and Personality Dynamics.* New York. [119]

Nice, M. M. (1943). Studies in the life history of the song sparrow. *Trans. Linn. Soc. N.Y.* **6**, 1–328. [26, 35, 37, 47, 49, 51]

Nicholson, E. M. (1927). *How Birds Live.* London. [7, 64]

Nicholson, E. M. and Koch, L. (1936). *Songs of Wild Birds.* London. [65]

Nicolai, J. (1959). Familien Tradition in der Gesangsentwicklung des Gimpels. *J. Orn.* **100**, 39–46. [88]

Noble, R. (1931). The varying length of lark song. *Scot. Nat.* **188**, 47–54. [6]

Owen, R. (1866). *The Anatomy of Vertebrates,* II. London. [113]

Palmgren, P. (1932). Ein Versuch zur Registrierung der Intensitätsvariationen des Vogelgesanges in lauf einestages. *Ornis fenn.* **9**, 68–74. [53]

Palmgren, P. (1949). On the diurnal rhythm of activity and rest in birds. *Ibis*, **91**, 561–576. [53]

Peterson, R. T. (1934). *Field Guide to Birds of New York.* New York. [99]

Peterson, R. T. (1941). *Field Guide to Western Birds.* New York. [99]

Potter, R. K., Kopp, G. A. and Green, H. C. (1947). *Visible Speech.* New York. [ix, 112, 116]

Poulsen, H. (1954). On the song of the Linnet (*Carduelis cannabina*). *Dansk. orn. Foren. Tidsskr.* **48**, 32–7. [10]

Poulsen, H. (1958). The calls of the chaffinch, *Fringilla coelebs* L., in Denmark. *Dansk orn. Foren. Tidsskr.* **52**, 89–105. [16, 35, 37]

Poulsen, H. (1959). Song-learning in the domestic canary. *Z. Tierpsychol.* **16**, 173–8. [86]

Pumphrey, R. J. (1948). The sense organs of birds. *Ibis*, **90**, 171–99. [122]

Pumphrey, R. J. (1958). Hearing in man and animals. *Proc. Roy. Instn G.B.* **37**, 93–118.

Pumphrey, R. J. (1961). Hearing in birds, in Marshall (1960–1), vol. 2. [121, 122, 125]

Pycraft, W. P. (1910). *A History of Birds.* London. [107]

Quaintance, C. W. (1938). Context, meaning and possible origin of male song in the Brown Towhee. *Condor*, **40**, 97–101. [44]

Redfield, J. (1935). *Music: A Science and an Art.* New York. [1]

Ridpath, M. G. (1959). Report on international colloquium on acoustic and other methods of preventing bird damage to crops (unpublished memorandum. Quoted by permission). [21]

Rüppell, W. (1933). Physiologie und Akustik der Vogelstimme. *J. Orn.* **81**, 433–542. [107, 111, 118]

Sauer, F. (1954). Die Entwicklung der Lautäusserungen vom Ei ab schalldicht gehaltener Dorngrasmücken (*Sylvia c. communis* Latham) mit später isolierten und mit wildleben Artgenossen. *Z. Tierpsychol.* **11**, 10–93. [27, 36, 37, 40]

Sauer, F. (1955). Über Variationen der Artgesänge bei Grasmücken. *J. Orn.* **96**, 129–46. [27]

Saunders, A. A. (1929). Bird song. *N.Y. S. Mus. Handb.* **7**, 1–202. [6]

Saunders, A. A. (1935). *A Guide to Bird Songs.* New York. [xii]

Saunders, A. A. (1951). The song of the song sparrow. *Wilson Bull.* **63**, 99–108. [100]

Schufeldt, R. W. (1890). The Myology of the Raven. London. [113]

Schwartzkopff, J. (1949). Über Sitz und Leistung von Gehör und Vibrationssinn bei Vögeln. *Z. vergl. Physiol.* **31**, 527. [124]

Schwartzkopff, J. (1952). Über den Gehörsinn der Vögel. *J. Orn.* **93**, 91–103.

Schwartzkopff, J. (1955 a). Schallsinnesorgane, ihre Funktion und biologisches Bedeutung bei Vögeln. *Acta 11th Congr. Int. Orn.* Basle, 189–208. [121, 122]

Schwartzkopff, J. (1955 b). On the hearing of birds. *Auk,* **72**, 340–7. [121, 127]

Schwartzkopff, J. (1957). Die Grössenverhältnisse von Trommelfell columella-Fussplatte und Schnecke bei Vögeln verschiedenen Gewichts. *Z. Morph. Ökol. Tiere,* **45**, 365–78. [122]

Sick, H. (1939). Ueber die Dialektbildung beim 'Regenrauf' des Buchfinken. *J. Orn.* **87**, 568–92. [101]

Skutch, A. F. (1940). Social and sleeping habits of Central American Wrens. *Auk,* **57**, 293–312. [50]

Skutch, A. F. (1954). Life histories of Central American birds. *Pacific Coast Avifauna,* no. 31. [49, 53]

Slud, P. (1958). Observations on the nightingale wren in Costa Rica. *Condor,* **60**, 243–51. [100]

Smith, R. L. (1959). The songs of the grasshopper sparrow. *Wilson Bull.* **71**, 141–52. [48]

Snow, D. W. (1956). The dance of the Manakins. *Anim. Kingd.* **59**, 86–91. [50]

Snow, D. W. (1958). *A Study of Blackbirds.* London. [16, 21, 37]

Sotovalta, O. (1956). Analysis of the song patterns of two Sprosser nightingales *Luscinia luscinia* L. *Ann. Soc. Zool. Botan. Fenn. Vanamo,* **17**, 1–31. [90]

Stanford, J. K. (1945). Variations in birds' songs and call notes in different localities. *Ibis,* **87**, 102–3. [99]

Stein, R. S. (1956). A comparative study of advertising song in the Hyocichla thrushes. *Auk,* **73**, 503–12. [105]

Stevens, S. S. (1950). Introduction: a definition of communication. In Proc. Speech Communication Conference, Massachusetts Institute of Technology. *J. Acoust. Soc. Amer.* **22**, 689–90. [7]

Stevens, S. S. and Davis, H. (1938). *Hearing: Its Psychology and Physiology.* New York. [29, 62, 121]

Thielcke, G. (1960). Mischgesang der Baumlaüfer *Certhia brachydactyla* und *C. familiaris. J. Orn.* **101**, 289–90. [99]

Thielcke-Poltz, H. and Thielcke, G. (1960). Akustisches Lernen verschieden alter schallisolierter Amseln (*Turdus merula* L.) und die Entwicklung erlernter Motive ohne und mit künstlichem Einfluss Testosteron. *Z. Tierpsychol.* **17**, 211–44. [88]

Thomson, J. A. (1923). *The Biology of Birds.* London. [113]

Thorpe, W. H. (1955). Comments on 'The Bird Fancyer's Delight' together with notes on imitation in the subsong of the chaffinch. *Ibis,* **97**, 247–51. [65]

Thorpe, W. H. (1956). *Learning and Instinct in Animals.* London. [10, 11, 63]

Thorpe, W. H. (1957). Note on the identification of Savi's grasshopper and river warblers by means of song. *Brit. Birds,* **50**, 169–71. [95]

Thorpe, W. H. (1958a). The learning of song patterns by birds, with especial reference to the song of the chaffinch, *Fringilla coelebs. Ibis,* **100**, 535–70. *This paper is cited so frequently that references to it are not indexed.*

Thorpe, W. H. (1958b). Further studies on the process of song learning in the chaffinch (*Fringilla coelebs gengleri*). *Nature, Lond.,* **182**, 554–7. [65, 77, 84]

Thorpe, W. H. (1959). Talking birds and the mode of action of the vocal apparatus of birds. *Proc. Zool. Soc. Lond.* **132**, 441–55. [61, 110, 114, 115, 116, 117, 118]

Thorpe, W. H. and Lade, B. I. (1961). I and II. The songs of some families of the order Passeriformes. *Ibis,* **103a**, 231–59. [xii, 57, 58, 60]

Thorpe, W. H. and Pilcher, P. M. (1958). The nature and characteristics of subsong. *Brit. Birds,* **51**, 509–14. [64, 65, 68, 69]

Ticehurst, C. B. (1938). *A Systematic Review of the Genus* Phylloscopus. British Museum, London. [99]

Tinbergen, N. (1939). The behaviour of the snow bunting in spring. *Trans. Linn. Soc. N.Y.* **5**, 1–95. [19, 48]

Tinbergen, N. (1953). *The Herring Gull's World.* London. [18, 37, 47]

Trainer, J. E. (1946). The auditory acuity of certain birds. Thesis, Cornell Univ. [123]

Tschanz, B. B. (1959). Zur Brutbiologie der Trottellumme (*Uria aalge aalge* Pont.). *Inaugural dissertation.* Brill, Leiden. [47]

Tyne, J. van and Berger, S. J. (1959). *Fundamentals of Ornithology.* New York. [49, 51]

Vaurie, C. (1959). *Birds of the Palearctic Fauna.* London. [99]

Voigt, A. (1950). *Excursionsbuch zum Studium der Vogelstimmen.* 11th edn. Heidelberg. [96]

Voipio, P. (1952). Disguised calls of birds as defence mechanisms. *Ornis fenn.* **29**, 63–7. (Finnish, with English abstract.) [32]

Wassiljew, Ph. (1933). Uber das Tonunterscheidungsvermögen der Vögel für die hohen Töne. *Z. vergl. Physiol.* **19**, 424–38. [123]

Wever, E. G. (1949). *The Theory of Hearing.* New York and London. [121]

135

Wever, E. G. and Bray, C. W. (1936). Hearing in the pigeon as studied by the electrical responses of the inner ear. *J. Comp. Psychol.* **22**, 353–63. [123]

Whitman, C. O. (1919). *The Behaviour of Pigeons.* Posthumous works of C. O. Whitman, **3**, 1–161, ed. A. H. Carr, *Publ. Carnegie Inst.* 257. [37]

Witherby, H. F., Jourdain, C. F. R., Ticehurst, N. F. and Tucker, B. W. (1948). *A Handbook of British Birds.* London. [100]

GENERAL INDEX

INDEX OF BIRDS